Essential Hymn Collection

kevin mayhew

We hope you enjoy *Essential Hymn Collection*. Further copies are available from your local Kevin Mayhew stockist.

In case of difficulty, or to request a catalogue,
please contact the publisher direct by writing to:

The Sales Department
KEVIN MAYHEW LTD
Buxhall
Stowmarket
Suffolk IP14 3BW

Phone 01449 737978
Fax 01449 737834
E-mail info@kevinmayhewltd.com

First published in Great Britain in 2002 by Kevin Mayhew Ltd.

© Copyright 2002 Kevin Mayhew Ltd.

ISBN 1 84003 957 4
ISMN M 57024 114 9
Catalogue No: 1413214

0 1 2 3 4 5 6 7 8 9

Cover design by Angela Selfe
Cover photograph by Nicky Dillon, Lambourn, Berkshire

Printed and bound in Great Britain

Important Copyright Information

The Publishers wish to express their gratitude to the copyright owners who have granted permission to include their copyright material in this book. Full details are indicated on the respective pages.

The **words** of most of the songs in this publication are covered by a **Church Copyright Licence** which is available from Christian Copyright Licensing International. This allows local church reproduction on overhead projector acetates, in service bulletins, songsheets, audio/visual recording and other formats.

The **music** in this book is covered by the additional **Music Reproduction Licence** which is issued by CCLI in the territories of Europe and Australasia. You may photocopy the music and words of the songs in the book provided:

You hold a current Music Reproduction Licence from CCLI.

The copyright owner of the song you intend to photocopy is included in the Authorised Catalogue List which comes with your Music Reproduction Licence.

The Music Reproduction Licence is **not** currently available in the USA or Canada.

Full details of CCLI can be obtained from their Web site (www.ccli.com) or you can contact them direct at the following offices:

Christian Copyright Licensing (Europe) Ltd
PO Box 1339, Eastbourne, East Sussex, BN21 1AD, UK
Tel: +44 (0)1323 417711; Fax: +44 (0)1323 417722; E-mail: info@ccli.co.uk

CCL Asia-Pacific Pty Ltd (Australia and New Zealand)
PO Box 6644, Baulkham Hills Business Centre, NSW 2153, Australia
Tel: +61 (02) 9894-5386; Toll Free Phone: 1-800-635-474
Fax: +61 (02) 9894-5701; Toll Free Fax: 1-800-244-477
E-mail executive@ccli.co.au

Christian Copyright Licensing Inc
17201 NE Sacramento Street, Portland, Oregon 97230, USA
Tel: +1 (503) 257 2230; Toll Free Phone: 1 (800) 234 2446;
Fax: +1 (503) 257 2244; E-mail executive@ccli.com

Please note, all texts and music in this book are protected by copyright and if you do <u>not</u> possess a licence from CCLI they may <u>not</u> be reproduced in any way for sale or private use without the consent of the copyright owner.

Foreword

In *Essential Hymn Collection* it has been our aim to gather together hymns and songs which are universally loved by Christians, thus providing a collection that can be used comfortably by all who raise their voice in worship of God.

It is something Jesus would have been familiar with in the temple, and he certainly sang at the Last Supper, for, according to Matthew: 'After psalms had been sung they left for the Mount of Olives.'

And the apostle Paul, writing to the Ephesians, was another enthusiast: 'Sing hymns and psalms to the Lord with praise in your hearts.'

What a wonderful faith we share!

THE PUBLISHER

1 Abba, Father, let me be

Dave Bilbrough

Dave Bilbrough
arr. Christopher Tambling

2 Abide with me

Henry Francis Lyte (1793-1847)

William Henry Monk (1823-1889)

EVENTIDE 10 10 10 10

1. A - bide with me, fast falls the e - ven - tide; the dark - ness deep - ens; Lord, with me a - bide: when o - ther help - ers fail, and com - forts flee, help of the help - less, O a - bide with me.

2. Swift to its close ebbs out life's little day;
   earth's joys grow dim, its glories pass away;
   change and decay in all around I see;
   O thou who changest not, abide with me.

3. I need thy presence ev'ry passing hour;
   what but thy grace can foil the tempter's pow'r?
   Who like thyself my guide and stay can be?
   Through cloud and sunshine, Lord, abide with me.

4. I fear no foe with thee at hand to bless;
   ills have no weight, and tears no bitterness.
   Where is death's sting? Where, grave, thy victory?
   I triumph still, if thou abide with me.

5. Hold thou thy cross before my closing eyes;
   shine through the gloom, and point me to the skies;
   heav'n's morning breaks, and earth's vain shadows flee;
   in life, in death, O Lord, abide with me.

3 A great and mighty wonder

St Germanus (c.634-c.734) trans.
John Mason Neale (1818-1866)

German carol melody, harmonies based
on Michael Praetorius (1571-1621) alt.

ES IST EIN' ROS' ENTSPRUNGEN 76 76 676

1. A great and migh-ty won - der, a full and ho - ly cure!
The Vir-gin bears the in - fant with vir-gin hon - our pure:
Refrain
Re - peat the hymn a - gain! 'To God on high be
glo - ry, and peace on earth shall reign.'

2. The Word becomes incarnate,
   and yet remains on high;
   and cherubim sing anthems
   to shepherds from the sky:

3. While thus they sing your monarch,
   those bright angelic bands,
   rejoice, ye vales and mountains,
   ye oceans, clap your hands:

4. Since all he comes to ransom
   by all be he adored,
   the infant born in Bethl'em,
   the Saviour and the Lord:

4 All creatures of our God and King

William Henry Draper (1855-1933) alt.
based on the 'Cantico di Frate Sole' of
St. Francis of Assisi (1182-1226)

'Geistliche Kirchengesang', Cologne (1623)
arr. Ralph Vaughan Williams (1872-1958)

LASST UNS ERFREUEN   88 44 88 and Alleluias

1. All crea-tures of our God and King, lift up your voice and with us

sing al - le - lu - ia, al - le - lu - ia! Thou

burn-ing sun with gol - den beam, thou sil- ver moon with sof - ter

gleam: O praise him, O praise him, al - le -

Unison

lu - ia, al - le - lu - ia, al - le - lu - ia!

2. Thou rushing wind that art so strong,
   ye clouds that sail in heav'n along,
   O praise him, alleluia!
   Thou rising morn, in praise rejoice,
   ye lights of evening, find a voice:

3. Thou flowing water, pure and clear,
   make music for thy Lord to hear,
   alleluia, alleluia!
   Thou fire so masterful and bright,
   that givest us both warmth and light:

4. Dear mother earth, who day by day
   unfoldest blessings on our way,
   O praise him, alleluia!
   The flow'rs and fruits that in thee grow,
   let them his glory also show.

5. All you with mercy in your heart,
   forgiving others, take your part,
   O sing ye, alleluia!
   Ye who long pain and sorrow bear,
   praise God and on him cast your care:

6. And thou, most kind and gentle death,
   waiting to hush our latest breath,
   O praise him, alleluia!
   Thou leadest home the child of God,
   and Christ our Lord the way hath trod:

7. Let all things their Creator bless,
   and worship him in humbleness,
   O praise him, alleluia!
   Praise, praise the Father, praise the Son,
   and praise the Spirit, Three in One.

5 Alleluia, alleluia, give thanks to the risen Lord

Donald Fishel, alt.

Donald Fishel (b.1950)
arr. Andrew Moore

Refrain
Capo 3
Unison

Al-le-lu-ia, al-le-lu-ia, give thanks to the ri-sen Lord, al-le-lu-ia, al-le-lu-ia, give praise to his name.

1. Je-sus is Lord of all the earth.

He is the King of cre-a-tion.

2. Spread the good news o'er all the earth.
   Jesus has died and is risen.

3. We have been crucified with Christ.
   Now we shall live for ever.

4. God has proclaimed the just reward:
   'Life for us all, alleluia!'

5. Come, let us praise the living God,
   joyfully sing to our Saviour.

6 Alleluia, alleluia, hearts to heaven and voices raise

Christopher Wordsworth (1807-1885)

Arthur Seymour Sullivan (1842-1900)

LUX EOI 87 87 D

1. Al - le - lu - ia, al - le - lu - ia, hearts to heav'n and voi - ces raise;

sing to God a hymn of glad -ness, sing to God a hymn of praise:

he who on the cross a vic - tim for the world's sal - va - tion bled,

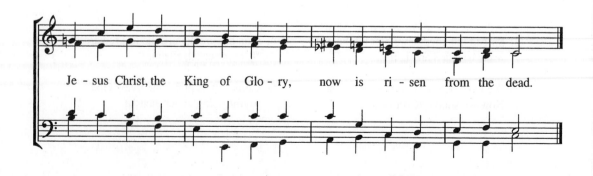

Je - sus Christ, the King of Glo - ry, now is ri - sen from the dead.

2. Christ is risen, Christ the first-fruits
   of the holy harvest field,
   which will all its full abundance
   at his second coming yield;
   then the golden ears of harvest
   will their heads before him wave,
   ripened by his glorious sunshine,
   from the furrows of the grave.

3. Christ is risen, we are risen;
   shed upon us heav'nly grace,
   rain, and dew, and gleams of glory
   from the brightness of thy face;
   that we, with our hearts in heaven,
   here on earth may fruitful be,
   and by angel-hands be gathered,
   and be ever, Lord, with thee.

4. Alleluia, alleluia,
   glory be to God on high;
   alleluia to the Saviour,
   who has gained the victory;
   alleluia to the Spirit,
   fount of love and sanctity;
   alleluia, alleluia,
   to the Triune Majesty.

7 Alleluia, sing to Jesus

William Chatterton Dix (1837-1898)
alt. the editors

Rowland Huw Pritchard (1811-1887)
arr. Ralph Vaughan Williams (1872-1958)

HYFRYDOL 87 87 D

1. Al - le - lu - ia, sing to Je - sus, his the

scep - tre, his the throne; al - le - lu - ia, his the

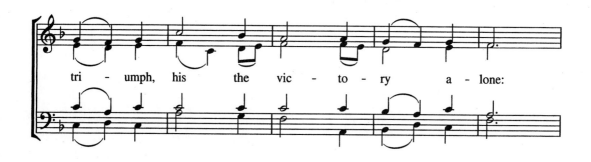

tri - umph, his the vic - to - ry a - lone:

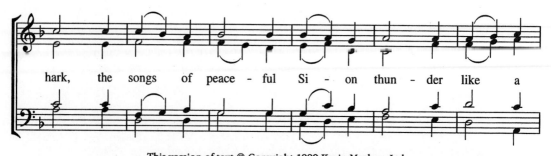

hark, the songs of peace - ful Si - on thun - der like a

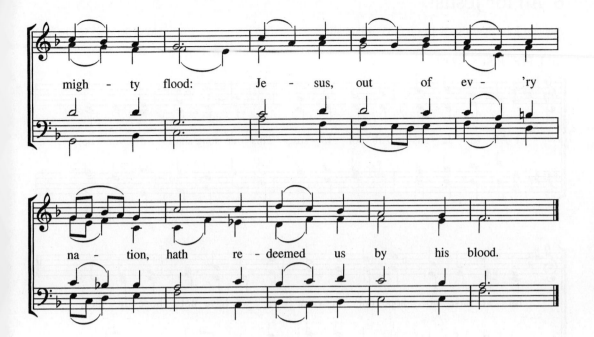

migh - ty flood: Je - sus, out of ev - 'ry

na - tion, hath re - deemed us by his blood.

2. Alleluia, not as orphans
   are we left in sorrow now;
   alleluia, he is near us,
   faith believes, nor questions how;
   though the cloud from sight received him
   when the forty days were o'er,
   shall our hearts forget his promise,
   'I am with you evermore'?

3. Alleluia, bread of angels,
   here on earth our food, our stay;
   alleluia, here the sinful
   come to you from day to day.
   Intercessor, friend of sinners,
   earth's redeemer, plead for me,
   where the songs of all the sinless
   sweep across the crystal sea.

4. Alleluia, King eternal,
   he the Lord of lords we own;
   alleluia, born of Mary,
   earth his footstool, heav'n his throne;
   he within the veil has entered
   robed in flesh, our great High Priest;
   he on earth both priest and victim
   in the Eucharistic Feast.

8 All for Jesus!

William John Sparrow-Simpson (1859-1952) alt.

John Stainer (1840-1901)

ALL FOR JESUS 87 87

1. All for Je-sus! All for Je-sus! This our song shall e-ver be;

for we have no hope nor Sa-viour if we have not hope in thee.

2. All for Jesus! thou wilt give us
   strength to serve thee hour by hour;
   none can move us from thy presence
   while we trust thy love and pow'r.

3. All for Jesus! at thine altar
   thou dost give us sweet content;
   there, dear Saviour, we receive thee
   in thy holy sacrament.

4. All for Jesus! thou hast loved us,
   all for Jesus! thou hast died,
   all for Jesus! thou art with us,
   all for Jesus, glorified!

5. All for Jesus! All for Jesus!
   This the Church's song shall be,
   till at last the flock is gathered
   one in love, and one in thee.

9 All glory, laud and honour

'Gloria, laus et honor' by St. Theodulph of Orleans (d.821)
trans. John Mason Neale (1818-1866)

Melchior Teschner (1584-1635)

ST THEODULPH 76 76 and Refrain

All glo-ry, laud and hon-our, to thee, Re-deem-er King, to
whom the lips of child-ren made sweet ho-san-nas ring.

1. Thou art the King of Is-rael, thou Da-vid's roy-al Son, who
in the Lord's name com-est, the King and bless-ed one.

2. The company of angels
   are praising thee on high,
   and mortals, joined with all things
   created, make reply.

3. The people of the Hebrews
   with palms before thee went:
   our praise and prayer and anthems
   before thee we present.

4. To thee before thy passion
   they sang their hymns of praise:
   to thee now high exalted
   our melody we raise.

5. Thou didst accept their praises,
   accept the prayers we bring,
   who in all good delightest,
   thou good and gracious king.

10 All hail the power of Jesus' name

Edward Perronet (1726-1792)
adapted by Michael Forster (b.1946)

William Shrubsole (1760-1806)

MILES LANE CM

1. All hail the pow'r of Je - sus' name, let an - gels pro - strate fall; bring forth the roy - al di - a - dem and crown him, crown him, crown him, crown him Lord of all.

2. Crown him, all martyrs of your God,
who from his altar call;
praise him whose way of pain you trod,
and crown him Lord of all.

3. O prophets faithful to his word,
in matters great and small,
who made his voice of justice heard,
now crown him Lord of all.

4. All sinners, now redeemed by grace,
who heard your Saviour's call,
now robed in light before his face,
O crown him Lord of all.

5. Let every tribe and every race
who heard the freedom call,
in liberation, see Christ's face
and crown him Lord of all.

6. Let every people, every tongue
to him their heart enthral:
lift high the universal song
and crown him Lord of all.

11 All heaven declares

Tricia Richards

Noel Richards

Majestically

1. All heav'n de-clares the glo-ry of the ri - sen Lord.

Who can com - pare with the beau-ty of the Lord?

For e-ver he will be the Lamb up-on the throne.

I glad-ly bow the knee and wor-ship him a-lone.

2. I will proclaim
the glory of the risen Lord.
Who once was slain
to reconcile us all to God.
For ever you will be
the Lamb upon the throne.
I gladly bow the knee
and worship you alone.

12 All I once held dear

Knowing you

Graham Kendrick
based on Philippians 3:8-12

Graham Kendrick (b.1950)
arr. Keith Stent

1. All I once held dear, built my life u - pon, all this world re - veres, and wars to own, all I once thought gain I have coun - ted loss; spent and worth - less now, com - pared to this. Know-ing you, Je-sus, know- ing you, there is no great - er thing. You're my all, you're the best, you're my

joy, my right-eous-ness, and I love you, Lord.

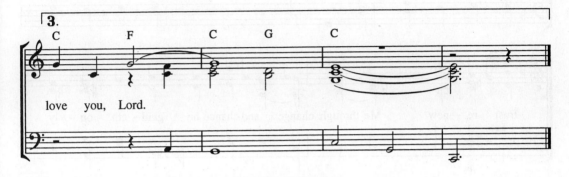

love you, Lord.

2. Now my heart's desire
   is to know you more,
   to be found in you
   and known as yours.
   To possess by faith
   what I could not earn,
   all-surpassing gift
   of righteousness.

3. Oh, to know the pow'r
   of your risen life,
   and to know you in
   your sufferings.
   To become like you
   in your death, my Lord,
   so with you to live
   and never die.

13 All my hope on God is founded

Paraphrased by Robert Bridges (1844-1930) alt.
based on 'Meine Hoffnung stehet feste'
by Joachim Neander (1650-1680)

Herbert Howells (1892-1983)

MICHAEL 87 87 33 7

1. All my hope on God is found - ed; he doth still my trust re - new. Me through change and chance he guid - eth, on - ly good and on - ly true. God un - known, he a - lone calls my heart to be his own.

2. Human pride and earthly glory,
   sword and crown betray his trust;
   what with care and toil he buildeth,
   tow'r and temple, fall to dust.
   But God's pow'r, hour by hour,
   is my temple and my tow'r.

3. God's great goodness aye endureth,
   deep his wisdom, passing thought:
   splendour, light and life attend him,
   beauty springeth out of naught.
   Evermore, from his store,
   new-born worlds rise and adore.

4. Still from earth to God eternal
   sacrifice of praise be done,
   high above all praises praising
   for the gift of Christ his Son.
   Christ doth call one and all:
   ye who follow shall not fall.

14 All over the world

Roy Turner

Roy Turner (b.1940)
arr. Andrew Moore

2. All over this land the Spirit is moving ...

3. All over the Church the Spirit is moving ...

4. All over us all the Spirit is moving ...

5. Deep down in my heart the Spirit is moving ...

15 All people that on earth do dwell

William Kethe (d.1594) from
'Day's Psalter' (1560) alt.

'Genevan Psalter' (1551), attributed to
Louis Bourgeois (c.1510-c.1561)

OLD HUNDREDTH LM

1. All peo-ple that on earth do dwell, sing

to the Lord with cheer - ful voice; him serve with fear, his

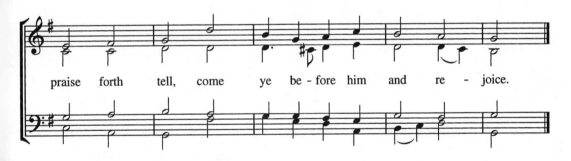

praise forth tell, come ye be - fore him and re - joice.

2. The Lord, ye know, is God indeed,
without our aid he did us make;
we are his folk, he doth us feed
and for his sheep he doth us take.

3. O enter then his gates with praise,
approach with joy his courts unto;
praise, laud and bless his name always,
for it is seemly so to do.

4. For why? the Lord our God is good:
his mercy is for ever sure;
his truth at all times firmly stood,
and shall from age to age endure.

5. To Father, Son and Holy Ghost,
the God whom heav'n and earth adore,
from us and from the angel-host
be praise and glory evermore.

16 All things bright and beautiful

Cecil Frances Alexander (1818-1895)

William Henry Monk (1823-1889)

ALL THINGS BRIGHT AND BEAUTIFUL 76 76 and Refrain

All things bright and beau - ti - ful, all crea - tures great and small,

all things wise and won - der-ful, the Lord God made them all.

1. Each lit - tle flow'r that o - pens, each lit - tle bird that sings, he

made their glow-ing col - ours, he made their ti - ny wings.

Org.

2. The purple-headed mountain,
   the river running by,
   the sunset and the morning
   that brightens up the sky.

3. The cold wind in the winter,
   the pleasant summer sun,
   the ripe fruits in the garden,
   he made them every one.

4. The tall trees in the greenwood,
   the meadows for our play,
   the rushes by the water,
   to gather ev'ry day.

5. He gave us eyes to see them,
   and lips that we might tell
   how great is God Almighty,
   who has made all things well.

17 All you who seek a comfort sure

'Quincunque centum quæritis' (18th century)
trans Edward Caswall (1814-1878) alt. the editors

Adapted from a melody
in 'Tochter Sion' (1741)

ST BERNARD CM

1. All you who seek a comfort sure in trouble and distress, whatever sorrow vex the mind, or guilt the soul oppress.

2. Jesus, who gave himself for you
   upon the cross to die,
   opens to you his sacred heart;
   O, to that heart draw nigh.

3. You hear how kindly he invites;
   you hear his words so blest:
   'All you that labour, come to me,
   and I will give you rest.'

4. What meeker than the Saviour's heart?
   As on the cross he lay,
   it did his murderers forgive,
   and for their pardon pray.

5. Jesus, the joy of saints on high,
   the hope of sinners here,
   attracted by those loving words
   to you I lift my prayer.

6. Wash then my wounds in that dear blood
   which forth from you does flow;
   by grace a better hope inspire,
   and risen life bestow.

18 Amazing grace

vs. 1-4: John Newton (1725-1807) alt;
v. 5: John Rees (1828-1900)

American Folk melody
arr. Richard Lloyd

AMAZING GRACE CM

1. A - maz - ing grace! How sweet the sound that saved a wretch like me. I once was lost, but now I'm found; was blind, but now I see.

2. 'Twas grace that taught my heart to fear,
and grace my fears relieved.
How precious did that grace appear
the hour I first believed.

3. Through many dangers, toils and snares
I have already come.
'Tis grace that brought me safe thus far,
and grace will lead me home.

4. The Lord has promised good to me,
his word my hope secures;
he will my shield and portion be
as long as life endures.

5. When we've been there a thousand years,
bright shining as the sun,
we've no less days to sing God's praise
than when we first begun.

19 And can it be

Charles Wesley (1707-1788)

Thomas Campbell (1824-1876)

SAGINA 88 88 88 extended

1. And can it be that I should gain an in - t'rest in the Sa - viour's blood? Died he for me, who caused his pain? For me, who him to death pur - sued? A - maz - ing love! How can it be that thou, my God, shouldst

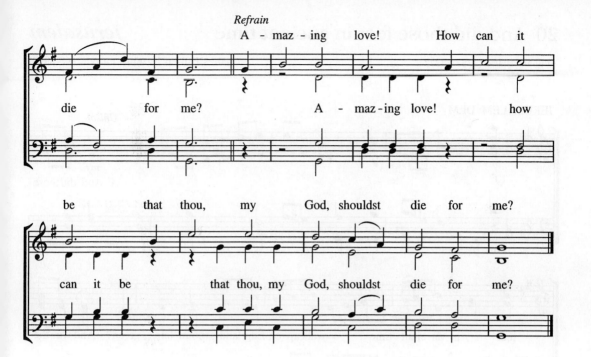

Refrain

A - maz - ing love! How can it die for me? A - maz - ing love! how be that thou, my God, shouldst die for me? can it be that thou, my God, shouldst die for me?

2. 'Tis myst'ry all! th'Immortal dies:
   who can explore his strange design?
   In vain the first-born seraph tries
   to sound the depths of love divine!
   'Tis mercy all! Let earth adore,
   let angel minds inquire no more.

3. He left his Father's throne above
   so free, so infinite his grace;
   emptied himself of all but love,
   and bled for Adam's helpless race;
   'tis mercy all, immense and free;
   for, O my God, it found out me.

4. Long my imprisoned spirit lay
   fast bound in sin and nature's night;
   thine eye diffused a quick'ning ray,
   I woke, the dungeon flamed with light;
   my chains fell off, my heart was free;
   I rose, went forth, and followed thee.

5. No condemnation now I dread;
   Jesus, and all in him, is mine!
   Alive in him, my living Head,
   and clothed in righteousness divine,
   bold I approach the eternal throne,
   and claim the crown, through Christ my own.

20 And did those feet in ancient time

Jerusalem

William Blake (1757-1827)

Charles Hubert Hastings Parry (1848-1918)

JERUSALEM DLM

1. And did those feet in an-cient time walk up-on Eng-land's moun-tains green? And was the ho - ly Lamb of God on Eng-land's plea-sant pas - tures seen? And did the coun - ten-ance di - vine shine forth up - on our cloud-ed hills? And was Je - ru - sa-lem build-ed here a -mong those dark sa-ta - nic mills?

2. Bring me my bow of burn-ing gold! Bring me my ar-rows of de - sire! Bring me my spear! O clouds un - fold! Bring me my cha - ri-ot of fire! I will not cease from men-tal fight, nor shall my sword sleep in my hand, till we have built Je - ru - sa - lem in Eng-land's green and plea - sant land.

Man.

Ped.

21 And now, O Father, mindful of the love

William Bright (1824-1901)

William Henry Monk (1823-1889)

UNDE ET MEMORES 10 10 10 10 10 10

1. And now, O Father, mindful of the love that bought us, once for all, on Cal-v'ry's tree, and hav-ing with us him that pleads a-bove, we here pre-sent, we here spread forth to thee that on-ly of-f'ring per-fect in thine eyes, the one true, pure, im-mor-tal sa-cri-fice.

2. Look, Father, look on his anointed face,
and only look on us as found in him;
look not on our misusings of thy grace,
our prayer so languid, and our faith so dim:
for lo, between our sins and their reward
we set the Passion of thy Son our Lord.

3. And then for those, our dearest and our best,
by this prevailing presence we appeal;
O fold them closer to thy mercy's breast,
O do thine utmost for their souls' true weal;
from tainting mischief keep them pure and clear,
and crown thy gifts with strength to persevere.

4. And so we come: O draw us to thy feet,
most patient Saviour, who canst love us still;
and by this food, so aweful and so sweet,
deliver us from ev'ry touch of ill:
in thine own service make us glad and free,
and grant us never more to part with thee.

22 A new commandment

v.1 unknown based on John 13:34-35;
vs. 2-4 Aniceto Nazareth
based on John 15 and 1 Corinthians 13

Unknown
arr. Andrew Moore

2. You are my friends if you do what I command you.
   Without my help you can do nothing. *(Repeat)*

3. I am the true vine, my Father is the gard'ner.
   Abide in me: I will be with you. *(Repeat)*

4. True love is patient, not arrogant nor boastful;
   love bears all things, love is eternal. *(Repeat)*

23 Angels from the realms of glory

James Montgomery (1771-1854)

French or Flemish melody
arr. Charles Wood (1866-1926)

IRIS 87 87 and Refrain

1. An-gels from the realms of glo - ry, wing your flight o'er all the earth;

ye who sang cre - a - tion's sto - ry now pro - claim Mes - si - ah's birth:

Refrain

Come

and wor - ship

Christ, the new-born King; come

and wor - ship, wor- ship Christ, the new - born King.

2. Shepherds, in the field abiding,
   watching o'er your flocks by night,
   God with us is now residing,
   yonder shines the infant Light:

3. Sages, leave your contemplations;
   brighter visions beam afar:
   seek the great Desire of Nations;
   ye have seen his natal star:

4. Saints before the altar bending,
   watching long in hope and fear,
   suddenly the Lord, descending,
   in his temple shall appear:

5. Though an infant now we view him,
   he shall fill his Father's throne,
   gather all the nations to him;
   ev'ry knee shall then bow down:

24 Angel-voices ever singing

Francis Pott (1832-1909) alt.

Edwin George Monk (1819-1900)

ANGEL VOICES 85 85 843

1. An - gel - voi - ces e - ver sing - ing round thy throne of light,
an - gel - harps for e - ver ring - ing, rest not day nor night;
thou-sands on - ly live to bless thee, and con - fess thee Lord of might.

2. Thou who art beyond the farthest
   mortal eye can see,
   can it be that thou regardest
   our poor hymnody?
   Yes, we know that thou art near us
   and wilt hear us constantly.

3. Yea, we know that thou rejoicest
   o'er each work of thine;
   thou didst ears and hands and voices
   for thy praise design;
   craftsman's art and music's measure
   for thy pleasure all combine.

4. In thy house, great God, we offer
   of thine own to thee;
   and for thine acceptance proffer,
   all unworthily,
   hearts and minds and hands and voices
   in our choicest psalmody.

5. Honour, glory, might and merit
   thine shall ever be,
   Father, Son and Holy Spirit,
   blessèd Trinity.
   Of the best that thou hast given
   earth and heaven render thee.

25 As the deer pants for the water

Martin Nystrom
based on Psalm 42:1-2

Martin Nystrom

Flowing

1. As the deer pants for the wa-ter, so my soul longs af - ter you.

You a - lone are my heart's de - sire and I long to wor - ship you.

Refrain

You a - lone are my strength, my shield, to you a - lone may my spi - rit yield.

You a - lone are my heart's de - sire and I long to wor - ship you.

2. I want you more than gold or silver,
only you can satisfy.
You alone are the real joy-giver
and the apple of my eye.

3. You're my friend and you are my brother,
even though you are a king.
I love you more than any other,
so much more than anything.

26 As we are gathered

John Daniels

John Daniels
arr. Andrew Moore

Unison

As we are ga-thered, Je-sus is here; one with each o-ther, Je-sus is here; joined by the Spi-rit, washed in the blood, part of the bo-dy, the church of God. As we are ga-thered, Je-sus is here; one with each o-ther, Je-sus is here.

27 As with gladness men of old

William Chatterton Dix (1837-1898) alt.

Adapted from Conrad Kocher (1786-1872)
by William Henry Monk (1823-1889)

DIX 77 77 77

1. As with glad-ness men of old did the guid-ing star be-hold,

as with joy they hailed its light, lead-ing on-ward, beam-ing bright;

so, most gra-cious Lord, may we e - ver-more be led to thee.

2. As with joyful steps they sped,
   to that lowly manger-bed,
   there to bend the knee before
   him whom heav'n and earth adore,
   so may we with willing feet
   ever seek thy mercy-seat.

3. As their precious gifts they laid,
   at thy manger roughly made,
   so may we with holy joy,
   pure, and free from sin's alloy,
   all our costliest treasures bring,
   Christ, to thee our heav'nly King.

4. Holy Jesu, ev'ry day
   keep us in the narrow way;
   and, when earthly things are past,
   bring our ransomed souls at last
   where they need no star to guide,
   where no clouds thy glory hide.

5. In the heav'nly country bright
   need they no created light,
   thou its light, its joy, its crown,
   thou its sun which goes not down;
   there for ever may we sing
   alleluias to our King.

28 At the Lamb's high feast we sing

'Ad regias Agni dapes' (7th century)
trans. Robert Campbell (1814-1868)
SALZBURG 77 77 D

Jacob Hintze (1622-1702); harmony by
Johann Sebastian Bach (1685-1750)

1. At the Lamb's high feast we sing praise to our vic-tor-ious King,
who hath washed us in the tide flow-ing from his pier-cèd side;
praise we him, whose love di-vine gives his sa-cred blood for wine,
gives his bo-dy for the feast, Christ the vic-tim, Christ the priest.

2. Where the paschal blood is poured,
   death's dark angel sheathes his sword;
   faithful hosts triumphant go
   through the wave that drowns the foe.
   Praise we Christ, whose blood was shed,
   paschal victim, paschal bread;
   with sincerity and love
   eat we manna from above.

3. Mighty victim from above,
   conqu'ring by the pow'r of love;
   thou hast triumphed in the fight,
   thou hast brought us life and light.
   Now no more can death appal,
   now no more the grave enthral:
   thou hast opened paradise,
   and in thee thy saints shall rise.

4. Easter triumph, Easter joy,
   nothing now can this destroy;
   from sin's pow'r do thou set free
   souls new-born, O Lord, in thee.
   Hymns of glory and of praise,
   risen Lord, to thee we raise;
   holy Father, praise to thee,
   with the Spirit, ever be.

29 At the name of Jesus

Caroline Maria Noel (1817-1877) alt.

William Henry Monk (1823-1889)

TUNE 1: EVELYNS 65 65 D

1. At the name of Je - sus ev - 'ry knee shall bow,
ev - 'ry tongue con - fess him King of glo - ry now;
'tis the Fa - ther's plea - sure we should call him Lord,
who, from the be - gin - ning, was the migh - ty Word.

2. At his voice creation
   sprang at once to sight,
   all the angels' faces,
   all the hosts of light,
   thrones and dominations,
   stars upon their way,
   all the heav'nly orders
   in their great array.

3. Humbled for a season,
   to receive a name
   from the lips of sinners
   unto whom he came,
   faithfully he bore it,
   spotless to the last,
   brought it back victorious
   when from death he passed.

4. Bore it up triumphant,
   with its human light,
   through all ranks of creatures
   to the central height,
   to the throne of Godhead,
   to the Father's breast,
   filled it with the glory
   of that perfect rest.

5. In your hearts enthrone him;
   there let him subdue
   all that is not holy,
   all that is not true;
   crown him as your captain
   in temptation's hour;
   let his will enfold you
   in its light and pow'r.

6. Truly, this Lord Jesus
   shall return again,
   with his Father's glory,
   with his angel train;
   for all wreaths of empire
   meet upon his brow,
   and our hearts confess him
   King of glory now.

Caroline Maria Noel (1817-1877) alt.   Michael Brierley (b.1932)

TUNE 2: CAMBERWELL 65 65 D

1. At the name of Je - sus ev - 'ry knee shall bow, ev - 'ry tongue con - fess him King of glo - ry now; 'tis the Fa - ther's plea - sure we should call him Lord, who, from the be - gin - ning, was the migh - ty Word.

To next verse   *Last time*

Word.   now.

30 Awake, my soul, and with the sun

Thomas Ken (1637-1711) alt.

François Hippolyte Barthélémon (1741-1808)

MORNING HYMN LM

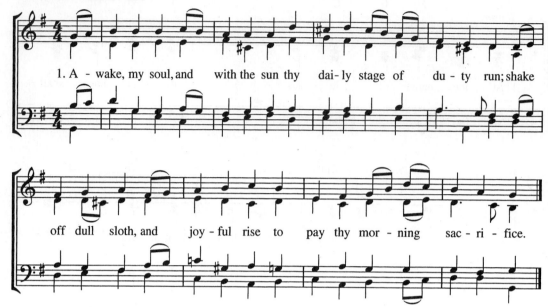

1. A - wake, my soul, and with the sun thy dai- ly stage of du - ty run; shake
off dull sloth, and joy - ful rise to pay thy mor - ning sac - ri - fice.

2. Redeem thy mis-spent time that's past,
   and live this day as if thy last;
   improve thy talent with due care;
   for the great day thyself prepare.

3. Let all thy converse be sincere,
   thy conscience as the noon-day clear;
   think how all-seeing God thy ways
   and all thy secret thoughts surveys.

4. Wake, and lift up thyself, my heart,
   and with the angels bear thy part,
   who all night long unwearied sing
   high praise to the eternal King.

PART 2

5. Glory to thee, who safe hast kept
   and hast refreshed me whilst I slept;
   grant, Lord, when I from death shall wake,
   I may of endless light partake.

6. Lord, I my vows to thee renew;
   disperse my sins as morning dew;
   guard my first springs of thought and will,
   and with thyself my spirit fill.

7. Direct, control, suggest, this day,
   all I design or do or say;
   that all my pow'rs, with all their might,
   in thy sole glory may unite.

This Doxology is sung after either part:

8. Praise God, from whom all blessings flow,
   praise him, all creatures here below,
   praise him above, angelic host,
   praise Father, Son and Holy Ghost.

31 Away in a manger

William James Kirkpatrick

William James Kirkpatrick (1838-1921)
arr. Richard Lloyd

CRADLE SONG 11 11 11 11

1. A - way in a man-ger, no crib for a bed, the lit-tle Lord Je - sus laid down his sweet head. The stars in the bright sky looked down where he lay, the lit-tle Lord Je-sus, a - sleep on the hay.

2. The cattle are lowing, the baby awakes,
   but little Lord Jesus no crying he makes.
   I love thee, Lord Jesus! Look down from the sky,
   and stay by my side until morning is nigh.

3. Be near me, Lord Jesus; I ask thee to stay
   close by me for ever, and love me, I pray.
   Bless all the dear children in thy tender care,
   and fit us for heaven, to live with thee there.

32 Be still, for the presence of the Lord

David J. Evans   David J. Evans (b.1957)

2. Be still, for the glory of the Lord is shining all around;
   he burns with holy fire, with splendour he is crowned.
   How awesome is the sight, our radiant King of light!
   Be still, for the glory of the Lord is shining all around.

3. Be still, for the power of the Lord is moving in this place;
   he comes to cleanse and heal, to minister his grace.
   No work too hard for him, in faith receive from him.
   Be still, for the power of the Lord is moving in this place.

33 Be still, my soul

Katherina von Schlegel (b.1697)
trans. Jane L. Borthwick alt.

Jean Sibelius (1865-1957)

FINLANDIA 10 10 10 10 10 10

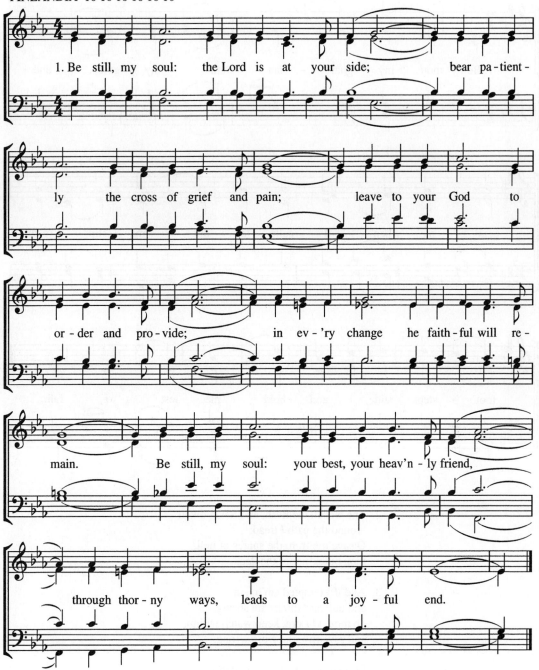

1. Be still, my soul: the Lord is at your side; bear pa-tient-ly the cross of grief and pain; leave to your God to or-der and pro-vide; in ev-'ry change he faith-ful will re-main. Be still, my soul: your best, your heav'n-ly friend, through thor-ny ways, leads to a joy-ful end.

2. Be still, my soul: your God will undertake
to guide the future as he has the past.
Your hope, your confidence let nothing shake,
all now mysterious shall be clear at last.
Be still, my soul: the tempests still obey
his voice, who ruled them once on Galilee.

3. Be still, my soul: the hour is hastening on
when we shall be for ever with the Lord,
when disappointment, grief and fear are gone,
sorrow forgotten, love's pure joy restored.
Be still, my soul: when change and tears are past,
all safe and blessèd we shall meet at last.

34 Be thou my guardian and my guide

Isaac Williams (1802-1865)

Melody by Isaac Smith (1734-1805)

ABRIDGE CM

1. Be thou my guard - ian and my guide, and hear me when I call; let not my slip - p'ry foot - steps slide, and hold me lest I fall.

2. The world, the flesh, and Satan dwell
around the path I tread;
O save me from the snares of hell,
thou quick'ner of the dead.

3. And if I tempted am to sin,
and outward things are strong,
do thou, O Lord, keep watch within,
and save my soul from wrong.

4. Still let me ever watch and pray,
and feel that I am frail;
that if the tempter cross my way,
yet he may not prevail.

35 Be thou my vision

Irish (c.8th century)
trans. Mary Byrne (1880-1931)
and Eleanor Hull (1860-1935)

Traditional Irish melody
arr. Colin Hand

SLANE 10 10 10 10

1. Be thou my vi - sion, O Lord of my heart,
naught be all else to me save that thou art;
thou my best thought in the day and the night,
wa - king or sleep - ing, thy pre - sence my light.

2. Be thou my wisdom, be thou my true word,
I ever with thee and thou with me, Lord;
thou my great Father, and I thy true heir;
thou in me dwelling, and I in thy care.

3. Be thou my breastplate, my sword for the fight,
be thou my armour, and be thou my might,
thou my soul's shelter, and thou my high tow'r,
raise thou me heav'nward, O Pow'r of my pow'r.

4. Riches I need not, nor all the world's praise,
thou mine inheritance through all my days;
thou, and thou only, the first in my heart,
high King of heaven, my treasure thou art!

5. High King of heaven, when battle is done,
grant heaven's joy to me, O bright heav'n's sun;
Christ of my own heart, whatever befall,
still be my vision, O Ruler of all.

36 Bind us together, Lord

Bob Gilman

Bob Gilman
arr. Andrew Moore

Refrain

Unison

Bind us to-ge-ther, Lord, bind us to-ge-ther with cords that can-not be bro-ken. Bind us to-ge-ther, Lord, bind us to-ge-ther, Lord, bind us to-geth-er in love.

1. There is on-ly one God,

there is on – ly one King.

There is on – ly one Bo – dy,

that is why we sing:

2. Fit for the glory of God,
   purchased by his precious Blood,
   born with the right to be free:
   Jesus the vict'ry has won.

3. We are the fam'ly of God,
   we are his promise divine,
   we are his chosen desire,
   we are the glorious new wine.

37 Blessed assurance

Frances Jane van Alstyne
(Fanny J. Crosby) (1820-1915)

Phoebe Palmer Knapp (1839-1908)

BLESSED ASSURANCE Irregular

1. Bles - sed as - sur - ance, Je - sus is mine: O what a

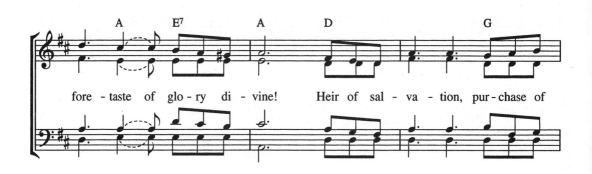

fore - taste of glo - ry di - vine! Heir of sal - va - tion, pur - chase of

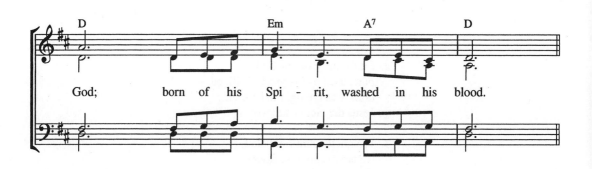

God; born of his Spi - rit, washed in his blood.

Refrain

This is my sto - ry, this is my song, prais - ing my

Sa - viour all the day long. This is my sto - ry, this is my

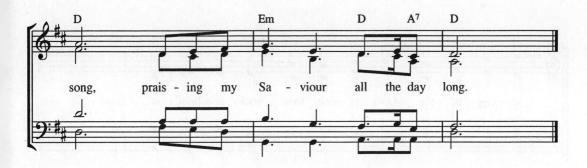

song, prais - ing my Sa - viour all the day long.

2. Perfect submission, perfect delight,
   visions of rapture burst on my sight;
   angels descending, bring from above
   echoes of mercy, whispers of love.

3. Perfect submission, all is at rest,
   I in my Saviour am happy and blest;
   watching and waiting, looking above,
   filled with his goodness, lost in his love.

38 Blest are the pure in heart

vs. 1 and 3: John Keble (1792-1866)
vs. 2 and 4: William John Hall's
'Psalms and Hymns' (1836) alt.

'Harmonischer Liederschatz' (1738) adapted
by William Henry Havergal (1793-1870)

FRANCONIA SM

1. Blest are the pure in heart, for they shall see our God; the

se - cret of the Lord is theirs, their soul is Christ's a - bode.

2. The Lord who left the heav'ns
   our life and peace to bring,
   to dwell in lowliness with us,
   our pattern and our King.

3. Still to the lowly soul
   he doth himself impart,
   and for his dwelling and his throne
   chooseth the pure in heart.

4. Lord, we thy presence seek;
   may ours this blessing be:
   give us a pure and lowly heart,
   a temple meet for thee.

39 Bread of heaven, on thee we feed

Josiah Conder (1789-1855)   William Dalrymple Maclagan (1826-1910)

BREAD OF HEAVEN 77 77 77

1. Bread of heav'n, on thee we feed, for thy flesh is meat in-deed;
e - ver may our souls be fed with this true and liv - ing bread;
day by day with strength sup -plied through the life of him who died.

2. Vine of heav'n, thy blood supplies
   this blest cup of sacrifice;
   Lord, thy wounds our healing give,
   to thy cross we look and live:
   Jesus, may we ever be
   grafted, rooted, built in thee.

40 Breathe on me, Breath of God

Edwin Hatch (1835-1889)
alt. the editors

Charles Lockhart (1745-1815)

CARLISLE SM

1. Breathe on me, Breath of God, fill me with life a-new, that as you love, so may I love, and do what you would do.

2. Breathe on me, Breath of God,
   until my heart is pure:
   until my will is one with yours
   to do and to endure.

3. Breathe on me, Breath of God,
   fulfil my heart's desire,
   until this earthly part of me
   glows with your heav'nly fire.

4. Breathe on me, Breath of God,
   so shall I never die,
   but live with you the perfect life
   of your eternity.

41 Brightest and best

Reginald Heber (1783-1826)   Joseph Francis Thrupp (1827-1867)

EPIPHANY 11 10 11 10

1. Brightest and best of the suns of the morning,
   dawn on our darkness and lend us thine aid;
   star of the east, the horizon adorning,
   guide where our infant Redeemer is laid.

2. Cold on his cradle the dew-drops are shining;
   low lies his head with the beasts of the stall;
   angels adore him in slumber reclining,
   Maker and Monarch and Saviour of all.

3. Say, shall we yield him, in costly devotion,
   odours of Edom, and off'rings divine,
   gems of the mountain, and pearls of the ocean,
   myrrh from the forest, or gold from the mine?

4. Vainly we offer each humble oblation,
   vainly with gifts would his favour secure:
   richer by far is the heart's adoration,
   dearer to God are the prayers of the poor.

42 Bright the vision that delighted

Richard Mant (1776-1848)   Richard Redhead (1820-1901)

LAUS DEO (REDHEAD NO. 46) 87 87

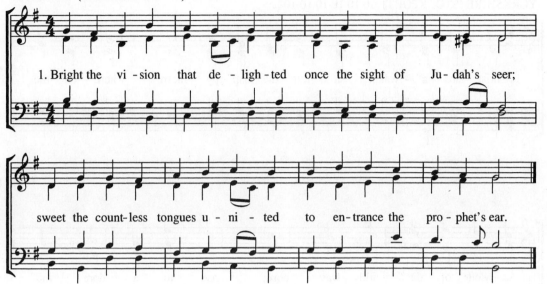

1. Bright the vi - sion that de - ligh - ted once the sight of Ju - dah's seer;
sweet the count-less tongues u - ni - ted to en - trance the pro - phet's ear.

2. Round the Lord in glory seated
   cherubim and seraphim
   filled his temple, and repeated
   each to each the alternate hymn:

3. 'Lord, thy glory fills the heaven;
   earth is with its fulness stored;
   unto thee be glory given,
   holy, holy, holy Lord.'

4. Heav'n is still with glory ringing,
   earth takes up the angels' cry,
   'Holy, holy, holy,' singing,
   'Lord of hosts, the Lord most high.'

5. With his seraph train before him,
   with his holy Church below,
   thus unite we to adore him,
   bid we thus our anthem flow:

6. 'Lord, thy glory fills the heaven;
   earth is with its fulness stored;
   unto thee be glory given,
   holy, holy, holy Lord.'

43 Christians, awake!

John Byrom (1692-1763) alt.

John Wainwright (1723-1768)

YORKSHIRE (STOCKPORT) 10 10 10 10 10 10

1. Christ - ians, a - wake! sa - lute the hap - py morn, where - on the

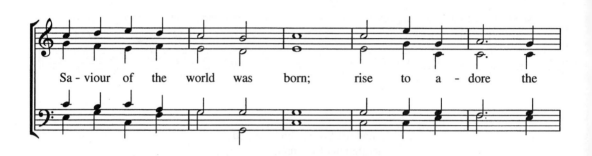

Sa - viour of the world was born; rise to a - dore the

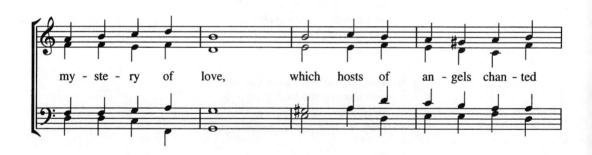

my - ste - ry of love, which hosts of an - gels chan - ted

from a - bove: with them the joy - ful ti - dings first be -

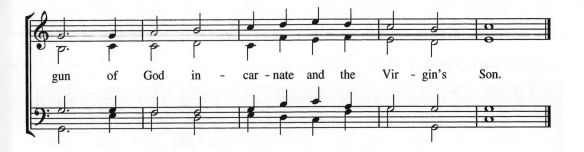

gun   of   God   in - car -nate and   the   Vir - gin's   Son.

2. Then to the watchful shepherds it was told,
   who heard th'angelic herald's voice, 'Behold,
   I bring good tidings of a Saviour's birth
   to you and all the nations on the earth:
   this day hath God fulfilled his promised word,
   this day is born a Saviour, Christ the Lord.'

3. He spake; and straightway the celestial choir
   in hymns of joy, unknown before, conspire;
   the praises of redeeming love they sang,
   and heav'n's whole orb with alleluias rang:
   God's highest glory was their anthem still,
   peace on the earth, in ev'ry heart good will.

4. To Bethl'em straight th'enlightened shepherds ran,
   to see, unfolding, God's eternal plan,
   and found, with Joseph and the blessèd maid,
   her Son, the Saviour, in a manger laid:
   then to their flocks, still praising God, return,
   and their glad hearts with holy rapture burn.

5. O may we keep and ponder in our mind
   God's wondrous love in saving lost mankind;
   trace we the babe, who hath retrieved our loss,
   from his poor manger to his bitter cross;
   tread in his steps, assisted by his grace,
   till our first heav'nly state again takes place.

6. Then may we hope, th'angelic hosts among,
   to sing, redeemed, a glad triumphal song:
   he that was born upon this joyful day
   around us all his glory shall display;
   saved by his love, incessant we shall sing
   eternal praise to heav'n's almighty King.

44 Christ is made the sure foundation

'Urbs beata Jerusalem' (c.7th century)
trans. John Mason Neale (1818-1866) alt.

Henry Purcell (1659-1695)
arr. E. Hawkins (1802-1868)

WESTMINSTER ABBEY 87 87 87

1. Christ is made the sure foun - da - tion, Christ the head and
cor - ner - stone, cho - sen of the Lord, and pre - cious,
bind - ing all the Church in one, ho - ly Zi - on's
help for e - ver, and her con - fi - dence a - lone.

2. To this temple, where we call you,
   come, O Lord of hosts, today;
   you have promised loving kindness,
   hear your servants as we pray,
   bless your people now before you,
   turn our darkness into day.

3. Hear the cry of all your people,
   what they ask and hope to gain;
   what they gain from you, for ever
   with your chosen to retain,
   and hereafter in your glory
   evermore with you to reign.

4. Praise and honour to the Father,
   praise and honour to the Son,
   praise and honour to the Spirit,
   ever Three and ever One,
   One in might and One in glory,
   while unending ages run.

45 Christ is our cornerstone

Latin (pre 9th century)
trans. John Chandler (1806-1876)

Samuel Sebastian Wesley (1810-1876)

HAREWOOD 66 66 44 44

1. Christ is our cor-ner-stone, on him a-lone we build; with his true saints a-lone the courts of heav'n are filled: on his great love our hopes we place of pre-sent grace and joys a-bove.

2. O then with hymns of praise
   these hallowed courts shall ring;
   our voices we will raise
   the Three in One to sing;
   and thus proclaim
   in joyful song,
   both loud and long,
   that glorious name.

3. Here, gracious God, do thou
   for evermore draw nigh;
   accept each faithful vow,
   and mark each suppliant sigh;
   in copious show'r
   on all who pray
   each holy day
   thy blessings pour.

4. Here may we gain from heav'n
   the grace which we implore;
   and may that grace, once giv'n,
   be with us evermore,
   until that day
   when all the blest
   to endless rest
   are called away.

46 Christ the Lord is risen again

Michael Weisse (c.1480-1534)
trans. Catherine Winkworth (1827-1878) alt.

Melody from 'Hundert Arien',
Dresden (1694)

WÜRTTEMBERG 77 77 with Alleluia

1. Christ the Lord is ris'n a - gain, Christ hath bro - ken ev - 'ry chain.
Hark, an - ge - lic voi - ces cry, sing - ing e - ver - more on high, Al - le - lu - ia.

2. He who gave for us his life,
   who for us endured the strife,
   is our paschal Lamb today;
   we too sing for joy, and say: Alleluia.

3. He who bore all pain and loss
   comfortless upon the cross,
   lives in glory now on high,
   pleads for us, and hears our cry: Alleluia.

4. He whose path no records tell,
   who descended into hell,
   who the strongest arm hath bound,
   now in highest heav'n is crowned. Alleluia.

5. He who slumbered in the grave
   is exalted now to save;
   now through Christendom it rings
   that the Lamb is King of kings. Alleluia.

6. Now he bids us tell abroad
   how the lost may be restored,
   how the penitent forgiv'n,
   how we too may enter heav'n. Alleluia.

7. Thou, our paschal Lamb indeed,
   Christ, thy ransomed people feed;
   take our sins and guilt away;
   let us sing by night and day: Alleluia.

47 Christ triumphant

Michael Saward (b.1932)

Michael Baughen (b.1930)

CHRIST TRIUMPHANT 85 85 and Refrain

1.Christ tri-um-phant, e-ver reign-ing, Sav-iour, Mas-ter, King, Lord of heav'n, our lives sus-tain-ing, hear us as we sing: Yours the glo-ry and the crown, the high re-nown, the e-ter-nal name.

2. Word incarnate, truth revealing,
   Son of Man on earth!
   Pow'r and majesty concealing
   by your humble birth:

3. Suff'ring servant, scorned, ill-treated,
   victim crucified!
   Death is through the cross defeated,
   sinners justified:

4. Priestly King, enthroned for ever
   high in heav'n above!
   Sin and death and hell shall never
   stifle hymns of love:

5. So, our hearts and voices raising
   through the ages long,
   ceaselessly upon you gazing,
   this shall be our song:

48 Christ, whose glory fills the skies

Charles Wesley (1707-1788)

Johann Gottlob Werner's 'Choralbuch',
Leipzig (1815)

RATISBON 77 77 77

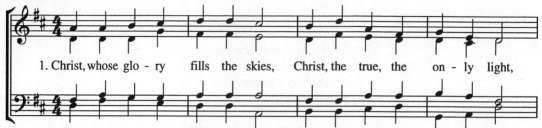

1. Christ, whose glo - ry fills the skies, Christ, the true, the on - ly light,

Sun of Righ-teous - ness, a - rise, tri - umph o'er the shades of night;

Day-spring from on high, be near; Day - star, in my heart ap - pear.

2. Dark and cheerless is the morn
   unaccompanied by thee;
   joyless is the day's return,
   till thy mercy's beams I see,
   till they inward light impart,
   glad my eyes, and warm my heart.

3. Visit then this soul of mine,
   pierce the gloom of sin and grief;
   fill me, radiancy divine,
   scatter all my unbelief;
   more and more thyself display,
   shining to the perfect day.

49 City of God, how broad and far

Samuel Johnson (1822-1882) alt.

Melody adapted from
Thomas Haweis (1734-1820)

RICHMOND CM

1. City of God, how broad and far outspread thy walls sublime! Thy free and loyal people are of ev - 'ry age and clime.

2. One holy Church, one mighty throng,
   one steadfast, high intent;
   one working band, one harvest-song,
   one King omnipotent.

3. How purely hath thy speech come down
   from earth's primeval youth!
   How grandly hath thine empire grown
   of freedom, love and truth!

4. How gleam thy watch-fires through the night
   with never-fainting ray!
   How rise thy tow'rs, serene and bright,
   to meet the dawning day!

5. In vain the surge's angry shock,
   in vain the drifting sands;
   unharmed upon th'eternal Rock
   th'eternal city stands.

50 Colours of day

Light up the fire

SueMcClellan, John Paculabo
and Keith Ryecroft

Sue McClellan (b.1951), John Paculabo (b.1946)
and Keith Ryecroft (b.1949) arr. Andrew Moore

1. Col - ours of day dawn in - to the mind, the sun has come up, the night is be - hind. Go down in the ci - ty, in - to the street, and let's give the mes - sage to the peo - ple we meet.

So light up the fire and let the flame burn,

o - pen the door, let Je - sus re - turn, take
seeds of his Spi - rit, let the fruit grow, tell the
peo - ple of Je - sus, let his love show.

2. Go through the park, on into the town;
   the sun still shines on; it never goes down.
   The light of the world is risen again;
   the people of darkness are needing our friend.

3. Open your eyes, look into the sky,
   the darkness has come, the sun came to die.
   The evening draws on, the sun disappears,
   but Jesus is living, and his Spirit is near.

51 Come down, O Love divine

'Discendi, amor santo' by Bianco da Siena (d.1434)
trans. Richard F. Littledale (1833-1890) alt.

Ralph Vaughan Williams (1872-1958)

DOWN AMPNEY 66 11 D

2. O let it freely burn,
   till earthly passions turn
   to dust and ashes in its heat consuming;
   and let thy glorious light
   shine ever on my sight,
   and clothe me round, the while my path illuming.

3. Let holy charity
   mine outward vesture be,
   and lowliness become mine inner clothing;
   true lowliness of heart,
   which takes the humbler part,
   and o'er its own shortcomings weeps with loathing.

4. And so the yearning strong,
   with which the soul will long,
   shall far outpass the pow'r of human telling;
   nor can we guess its grace,
   till we become the place
   wherein the Holy Spirit makes his dwelling.

52 Come, Holy Ghost, our souls inspire

vs. 1-3, 5: John Cosin (1594-1672)
after Rabanus Maurus (c.776-856) alt.
v. 4: Michael Forster (b.1946)

'Proper Sarum Melody'
arr. Andrew Moore

VENI, CREATOR SPIRITUS (MECHLIN) LM

1. Come, Ho - ly Ghost, our souls in-spire, and ligh-ten with ce - le - stial fire;

thou the a-noin - ting Spi - rit art, who dost thy sev'n - fold gifts im- part.

5. 'Praise to thy e - ter - nal me - rit,

Fa - ther, Son and Ho - ly Spi - rit.' A - men.

2. Thy blessèd unction from above
   is comfort, life, and fire of love;
   enable with perpetual light
   the dullness of our blinded sight.

3. Anoint and cheer our soilèd face
   with the abundance of thy grace:
   keep far our foes, give peace at home;
   where thou art guide no ill can come.

4. Show us the Father and the Son,
   in thee and with thee, ever one.
   Then through the ages all along,
   this shall be our unending song.

5. 'Praise to thy eternal merit,
   Father, Son and Holy Spirit.'
   Amen.

53 Come, let us join our cheerful songs

Isaac Watts (1674-1758) alt.

Henry Lahee (1826-1912)

NATIVITY CM

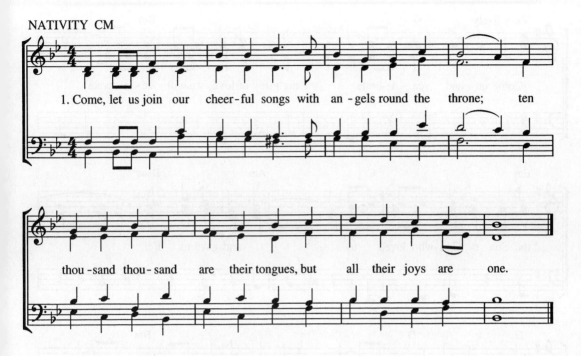

1. Come, let us join our cheer-ful songs with an-gels round the throne; ten

thou-sand thou-sand are their tongues, but all their joys are one.

2. 'Worthy the Lamb that died,' they cry,
   'to be exalted thus.'
   'Worthy the Lamb,' our lips reply,
   'for he was slain for us.'

3. Jesus is worthy to receive
   honour and pow'r divine;
   and blessings, more than we can give,
   be, Lord, for ever thine.

4. Let all creation join in one
   to bless the sacred name
   of him that sits upon the throne,
   and to adore the Lamb.

54 Come on and celebrate

Patricia Morgan
Dave Bankhead

Patricia Morgan
Dave Bankhead

Come on and ce-le-brate his gift of love, we will ce-le-brate the Son of God who loved us and gave us life. We'll shout your praise, O King, you give us joy no-thing else can bring; we'll give to you our of-fer-ing in ce-le-bra-tion praise. Come on and ce-le-brate, ce-le-brate, ce-le-brate and

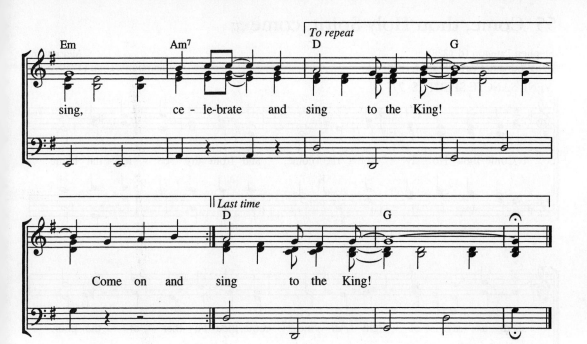

sing, ce - le-brate and sing to the King!

Come on and sing to the King!

55 Come, thou Holy Spirit, come

Stephen Langton (d.1228)
trans. Edward Caswall (1814-1878) alt.

Melody by
Samuel Webbe (1740-1816)

VENI, SANCTE SPIRITUS 777 D

1. Come, thou Ho - ly Spi - rit, come, and from thy ce - les - tial home

shed a ray of light di - vine; come, thou Fa - ther of the poor,

come, thou source of all our store, come, with - in our bo - soms shine.

2. Thou of comforters the best,
   thou the soul's most welcome guest,
   sweet refreshment here below;
   in our labour rest most sweet,
   grateful coolness in the heat,
   solace in the midst of woe.

3. O most blessèd Light divine,
   shine within these hearts of thine,
   and our inmost being fill,
   where thou art not, we have naught,
   nothing good in deed or thought,
   nothing free from taint of ill.

4. Heal our wounds, our strength renew;
   on our dryness pour thy dew;
   wash the stains of guilt away;
   bend the stubborn heart and will;
   melt the frozen, warm the chill;
   guide the steps that go astray.

5. On the faithful, who adore
   and confess thee, evermore
   in thy sev'nfold gifts descend,
   give them virtue's sure reward,
   give them thy salvation, Lord,
   give them joys that never end.

56 Come, thou long-expected Jesus

Charles Wesley (1707-1788)

John Stainer (1840-1901)

CROSS OF JESUS 87 87

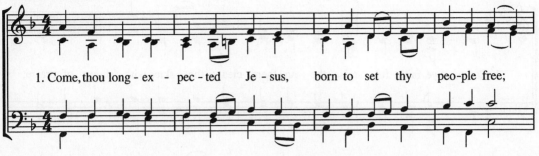

1. Come, thou long-ex - pec - ted Je - sus, born to set thy peo-ple free;

from our fears and sins re - lease us; let us find our rest in thee.

2. Israel's strength and consolation,
   hope of all the earth thou art;
   dear desire of ev'ry nation,
   joy of ev'ry longing heart.

3. Born thy people to deliver;
   born a child and yet a king;
   born to reign in us for ever;
   now thy gracious kingdom bring.

4. By thine own eternal Spirit,
   rule in all our hearts alone:
   by thine all-sufficient merit,
   raise us to thy glorious throne.

57 Come, ye faithful, raise the anthem

Job Hupton (1762-1849)
John Mason Neale (1818-1866) alt.

Melody by
Joachim Neander (1640-1680)

NEANDER (UNSER HERRSCHER) 87 87 87

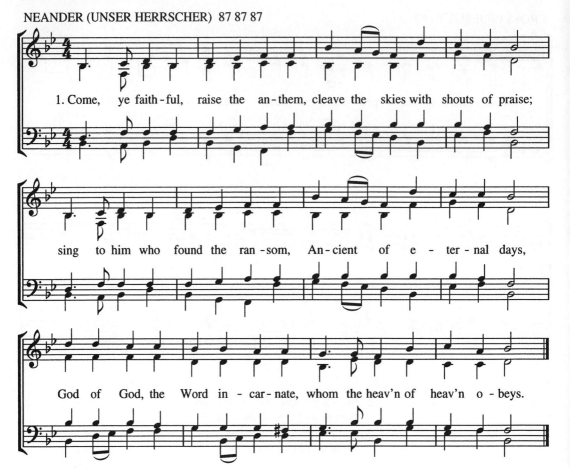

1. Come, ye faith-ful, raise the an-them, cleave the skies with shouts of praise;
sing to him who found the ran-som, An-cient of e-ter-nal days,
God of God, the Word in-car-nate, whom the heav'n of heav'n o-beys.

2. Ere he raised the lofty mountains,
   formed the seas or built the sky,
   love eternal, free and boundless,
   moved the Lord of Life to die,
   fore-ordained the Prince of princes
   for the throne of Calvary.

3. There, for us and our redemption,
   see him all his life-blood pour!
   There he wins our full salvation,
   dies that we may die no more;
   then arising, lives for ever,
   reigning where he was before.

4. High on yon celestial mountains
   stands his sapphire throne, all bright,
   midst unending alleluias
   bursting from the saints in light;
   Sion's people tell his praises,
   victor after hard-won fight.

5. Bring your harps, and bring your incense,
   sweep the string and pour the lay;
   let the earth proclaim his wonders,
   King of that celestial day;
   he the Lamb once slain is worthy,
   who was dead and lives for ay.

6. Laud and honour to the Father,
   laud and honour to the Son,
   laud and honour to the Spirit,
   ever Three and ever One,
   consubstantial, co-eternal,
   while unending ages run.

58 Come, ye faithful, raise the strain

St John of Damascus (d. c.754)
trans. John Mason Neale (1816-1866) alt.

Arthur Henry Brown (1830-1926)

ST JOHN DAMASCENE 76 76 D

1. Come, ye faithful, raise the strain of triumphant gladness;
God hath brought his Israel into joy from sadness;
loosed from Pharaoh's bitter yoke Jacob's sons and daughters;
led them with unmoistened foot through the Red Sea waters.

2. 'Tis the spring of souls today;
   Christ hath burst his prison,
   and from three day's sleep in death
   as a sun hath risen:
   all the winter of our sins,
   long and dark, is flying
   from his light, to whom we give
   laud and praise undying.

3. Now the queen of seasons, bright
   with the day of splendour,
   with the royal feast of feasts,
   comes its joy to render;
   comes to glad Jerusalem,
   who with true affection
   welcomes in unwearied strains
   Jesu's resurrection.

4. Alleluia now we cry
   to our King immortal,
   who triumphant burst the bars
   of the tomb's dark portal;
   Alleluia, with the Son,
   God the Father praising;
   Alleluia yet again
   to the Spirit raising.

59 Come, ye thankful people, come

Henry Alford (1810-1871) alt.

George Job Elvey (1816-1893)

ST GEORGE'S WINDSOR 77 77 D

1. Come, ye thankful people, come, raise the song of harvest-home! All is safely gathered in, ere the winter storms begin; God, our maker, doth provide for our wants to be supplied; come to God's own temple, come; raise the song of harvest-home!

2. We ourselves are God's own field,
   fruit unto his praise to yield;
   wheat and tares together sown,
   unto joy or sorrow grown;
   first the blade and then the ear,
   then the full corn shall appear:
   grant, O harvest Lord, that we
   wholesome grain and pure may be.

3. For the Lord our God shall come,
   and shall take his harvest home,
   from his field shall purge away
   all that doth offend, that day;
   give his angels charge at last
   in the fire the tares to cast,
   but the fruitful ears to store
   in his garner evermore.

4. Then, thou Church triumphant, come,
   raise the song of harvest-home;
   all be safely gathered in,
   free from sorrow, free from sin,
   there for ever purified
   in God's garner to abide:
   come, ten thousand angels, come,
   raise the glorious harvest-home!

60 Crown him with many crowns

Matthew Bridges (1800-1894) George Job Elvey (1816-1893)

DIADEMATA DSM

1. Crown him with ma-ny crowns, the Lamb up-on his throne, hark, how the heav'n-ly an-them drowns all mu-sic but its own: a-wake, my soul, and sing of him who died for thee, and hail him as thy match-less King through all e-ter-ni-ty.

2. Crown him the Virgin's Son,
   the God incarnate born,
   whose arm those crimson trophies won
   which now his brow adorn;
   fruit of the mystic Rose,
   as of that Rose the Stem,
   the Root, whence mercy ever flows,
   the Babe of Bethlehem.

3. Crown him the Lord of love;
   behold his hands and side,
   rich wounds, yet visible above,
   in beauty glorified:
   no angel in the sky
   can fully bear that sight,
   but downward bends each burning eye
   at mysteries so bright.

4. Crown him the Lord of peace,
   whose pow'r a sceptre sways
   from pole to pole, that wars may cease,
   absorbed in prayer and praise:
   his reign shall know no end,
   and round his piercèd feet
   fair flow'rs of paradise extend
   their fragrance ever sweet.

5. Crown him the Lord of years,
   the Potentate of time,
   Creator of the rolling spheres,
   ineffably sublime.
   All hail, Redeemer, hail!
   for thou hast died for me;
   thy praise shall never, never fail
   throughout eternity.

61 Dear Lord and Father of mankind

John Greenleaf Whittier (1807-1892)   Charles Hubert Hastings Parry (1848-1918)

REPTON 86 88 6

1. Dear Lord and Father of mankind, forgive our foolish ways! Reclothe us in our rightful mind, in purer lives thy service find, in deeper rev-'rence praise, in deeper rev-'rence praise.

2. In simple trust like theirs who heard,
   beside the Syrian sea,
   the gracious calling of the Lord,
   let us, like them, without a word,
   rise up and follow thee,
   rise up and follow thee.

3. O Sabbath rest by Galilee!
   O calm of hills above,
   where Jesus knelt to share with thee
   the silence of eternity,
   interpreted by love!
   Interpreted by love!

4. Drop thy still dews of quietness,
   till all our strivings cease;
   take from our souls the strain and stress,
   and let our ordered lives confess
   the beauty of thy peace,
   the beauty of thy peace.

5. Breathe through the heats of our desire
   thy coolness and thy balm;
   let sense be dumb, let flesh retire;
   speak through the earthquake, wind and fire,
   O still small voice of calm!
   O still small voice of calm!

62 Ding dong, merrily on high!

George Ratcliffe Woodward (1848-1934)

Traditional French melody
arr. Charles Wood (1866-1926)

BRANLE DE L'OFFICIAL 77 77 and Refrain

1. Ding dong, mer-ri-ly on high! In heav'n the bells are ring - ing;

ding dong, ve-ri-ly the sky is riv'n with an-gels sing - ing.

Glo - - - - ri-a, ho - san - na in ex - cel - sis!

2. E'en so here below, below,
   let steeple bells be swungen,
   and io, io, io,
   by priest and people sungen.

3. Pray you, dutifully prime
   your matin chime, ye ringers;
   may you beautifully rhyme
   your evetime song, ye singers.

63 Disposer supreme

J.B. de Santeuil (1630-1697)
trans. Isaac Williams (1802-1865) alt.

Thomas Ravencroft,
'Psalms' (1621)

OLD 104TH 10 10 11 11

1. Dis - po - ser su - preme, and Judge of the earth, thou choos-est for
thine the meek and the poor; to frail earth - en ves - sels, and
things of no worth, en - trust -ing thy rich - es which ay shall en - dure.

2. Those vessels are frail, though full of thy light,
   and many, once made, are broken and gone;
   thence brightly appeareth thy truth in its might,
   as through the clouds riven the lightnings have shone.

3. Like clouds are they borne to do thy great will,
   and swift as the winds about the world go:
   the Word with his wisdom their spirits doth fill;
   they thunder, they lighten, the waters o'erflow.

4. Their sound goeth forth, 'Christ Jesus the Lord!'
   then Satan doth fear, his citadels fall;
   as when the dread trumpets went forth at thy word,
   and one long blast shattered the Canaanites' wall.

5. O loud be their cry, and stirring their sound,
   to rouse us, O Lord, from slumber of sin;
   the lights thou hast kindled in darkness around,
   O may they awaken our spirits within.

6. All honour and praise, dominion and might,
   to God, Three in One, eternally be,
   who round us hath shed his own marvellous light,
   and called us from darkness his glory to see.

64 Do not be afraid

Gerard Markland
based on Isaiah 43.1-4

Gerard Markland (b.1953)
arr. Andrew Moore

Refrain
Unison

Do not be a-fraid, for I have re-deemed you.

I have called you by your name; you are

mine. *Fine* 1. When you walk through the wa-ters, I'll be

with you. You will ne-ver sink be-neath the waves. *D.C.*

2. When the fire is burning all around you,
   you will never be consumed by the flames.

3. When the fear of loneliness is looming,
   then remember I am at your side.

4. When you dwell in the exile of the stranger,
   remember you are precious in my eyes.

5. You are mine, O my child, I am your Father,
   and I love you with a perfect love.

65 Eternal Father, strong to save

William Whiting (1825-1878) alt.

John Bacchus Dykes (1823-1876)

MELITA 88 88 88

1. E - ter - nal Fa - ther, strong to save, whose arm doth bind the rest - less wave, who bidd'st the migh - ty o - cean deep its own ap - poin - ted lim - its keep: O hear us when we cry to thee for those in pe - ril on the sea.

2. O Saviour, whose almighty word
the winds and waves submissive heard,
who walkedst on the foaming deep,
and calm, amid its rage, didst sleep:
O hear us when we cry to thee
for those in peril on the sea.

3. O sacred Spirit, who didst brood
upon the waters dark and rude,
and bid their angry tumult cease,
and give, for wild confusion, peace:
O hear us when we cry to thee
for those in peril on the sea.

4. O Trinity of love and pow'r,
our brethren shield in danger's hour.
From rock and tempest, fire and foe,
protect them whereso'er they go,
and ever let there rise to thee
glad hymns of praise from land and sea.

66 Faithful Shepherd, feed me

Thomas Benson Pollock (1836-1896)   Friedrich Silcher (1789-1860)

PASTOR PASTORUM 65 65

1. Faith-ful Shep-herd, feed me in the pas-tures green;
faith-ful Shep-herd, lead me where thy steps are seen.

2. Hold me fast, and guide me
   in the narrow way;
   so, with thee beside me,
   I shall never stray.

3. Daily bring me nearer
   to the heav'nly shore;
   may my faith grow clearer,
   may I love thee more.

4. Hallow ev'ry pleasure,
   ev'ry gift and pain;
   be thyself my treasure,
   though none else I gain.

5. Day by day prepare me
   as thou seest best,
   then let angels bear me
   to thy promised rest.

67 Father, hear the prayer we offer

Maria Willis (1824-1908)

Traditional English melody adapted by
Ralph Vaughan Williams (1872-1958)

SUSSEX 87 87

1. Fa -ther, hear the prayer we of - fer: not for ease that prayer shall be, but for strength that we may e - ver live our lives cou - rage-ous - ly.

2. Not for ever in green pastures
   do we ask our way to be;
   but the steep and rugged pathway
   may we tread rejoicingly.

3. Not for ever by still waters
   Would we idly rest and stay;
   but would smite the living fountains
   from the rocks along our way.

4. Be our strength in hours of weakness,
   in our wand'rings be our guide;
   through endeavour, failure, danger,
   Father, be thou at our side.

68 Father, I place into your hands

Jenny Hewer

Jenny Hewer (b.1945)

1. Father, I place into your hands the things I cannot do. Father, I place into your hands the things that I've been through. Father, I place into your hands the way that I should go, for I know I always can trust you.

2. Father, I place into your hands
my friends and family.
Father, I place into your hands
the things that trouble me.
Father, I place into your hands
the person I would be,
for I know I always can trust you.

3. Father, we love to see your face,
we love to hear your voice.
Father, we love to sing your praise
and in your name rejoice.
Father, we love to walk with you
and in your presence rest,
for we know we always can trust you.

4. Father, I want to be with you
and do the things you do.
Father, I want to speak the words
that you are speaking too.
Father, I want to love the ones
that you will draw to you,
for I know that I am one with you.

69 Father of heaven, whose love profound

Edward Cooper (1770-1833)

John Bacchus Dykes (1823-1876)

RIEVAULX LM

1. Father of heav'n, whose love profound a ransom for our souls hath found, before thy throne we sinners bend, to us thy pard-'ning love extend.

2. Almighty Son, incarnate Word,
   our Prophet, Priest, Redeemer, Lord,
   before thy throne we sinners bend,
   to us thy saving grace extend.

3. Eternal Spirit, by whose breath
   the soul is raised from sin and death,
   before thy throne we sinners bend,
   to us thy quick'ning pow'r extend.

4. Thrice Holy! Father, Spirit, Son;
   mysterious Godhead, Three in One,
   before thy throne we sinners bend,
   grace, pardon, life, to us extend.

70 Father, we adore you

Terrye Coelho

Terrye Coelho (b.1952)
arr. Colin Hand

This may be sung in unison as a round, with entries at A, B and C

1. Father, we adore you, lay our lives before you. How we love you!

2. Jesus, we adore you,
   lay our lives before you.
   How we love you!

3. Spirit, we adore you,
   lay our lives before you.
   How we love you!

71 Father, we love you

Donna Adkins

Glorify your name

Donna Adkins (b.1940)
arr. Andrew Moore

1. Fa - ther, we love you, we wor - ship and a - dore you,
glo - ri - fy your name in all the earth.
Glo - ri - fy your name, glo - ri - fy your name,
glo - ri - fy your name in all the earth.

2. Jesus, we love you . . .

3. Spirit, we love you . . .

72 Fight the good fight

John Samuel Bewley Monsell (1811-1875) alt.

Melody attributed to
John Hatton (d.1793)

DUKE STREET LM

1. Fight the good fight with all thy might; Christ is thy strength, and Christ thy right; lay hold on life, and it shall be thy joy and crown e - ter - nal - ly.

2. Run the straight race through God's good grace,
   lift up thine eyes and seek his face;
   life with its way before us lies;
   Christ is the path, and Christ the prize.

3. Cast care aside, lean on thy guide;
   his boundless mercy will provide;
   trust, and thy trusting soul shall prove
   Christ is its life, and Christ its love.

4. Faint not nor fear, his arms are near;
   he changeth not, and thou art dear;
   only believe, and thou shalt see
   that Christ is all in all to thee.

73 Fill your hearts with joy and gladness

Timothy Dudley-Smith (b.1926)

Ludwig van Beethoven (1770-1827)
arr. Christopher Tambling

ODE TO JOY 87 87 D

1. Fill your hearts with joy and glad-ness, sing and praise your God and mine!
Great the Lord in love and wis-dom, might and ma-jes-ty di-vine!
He who framed the star-ry hea-vens knows and names them as they shine.
Fill your hearts with joy and glad-ness, sing and praise your God and mine!

2. Praise the Lord, his people, praise him!
Wounded souls his comfort know.
Those who fear him find his mercies,
peace for pain and joy for woe;
humble hearts are high exalted,
human pride and pow'r laid low.
Praise the Lord, his people, praise him!
Wounded souls his comfort know.

3. Praise the Lord for times and seasons,
cloud and sunshine, wind and rain;
spring to melt the snows of winter
till the waters flow again;
grass upon the mountain pastures,
golden valleys thick with grain.
Praise the Lord for times and seasons,
cloud and sunshine, wind and rain.

4. Fill your hearts with joy and gladness,
peace and plenty crown your days!
Love his laws, declare his judgements,
walk in all his words and ways;
he the Lord and we his children,
praise the Lord, all people, praise!
Fill your hearts with joy and gladness,
peace and plenty crown your days!

74 Firmly I believe and truly

John Henry Newman (1801-1890) alt.

Patrick Appleford (b.1925)

TUNE 1: ALTON 87 87

1. Firm - ly I be-lieve and tru - ly God is Three and God is One; and I next ac - know-ledge du - ly man -hood ta-ken by the Son.

2. And I trust and hope most ful - ly in the Sa-viour cru - ci - fied; and each thought and deed un - ru - ly do to death as he has died.

4. And I hold in ve - ne - ra - tion, for the love of him a - lone, ho - ly Church as his cre - a - tion, and her teach-ings as his own.

2nd time cut to verse 5

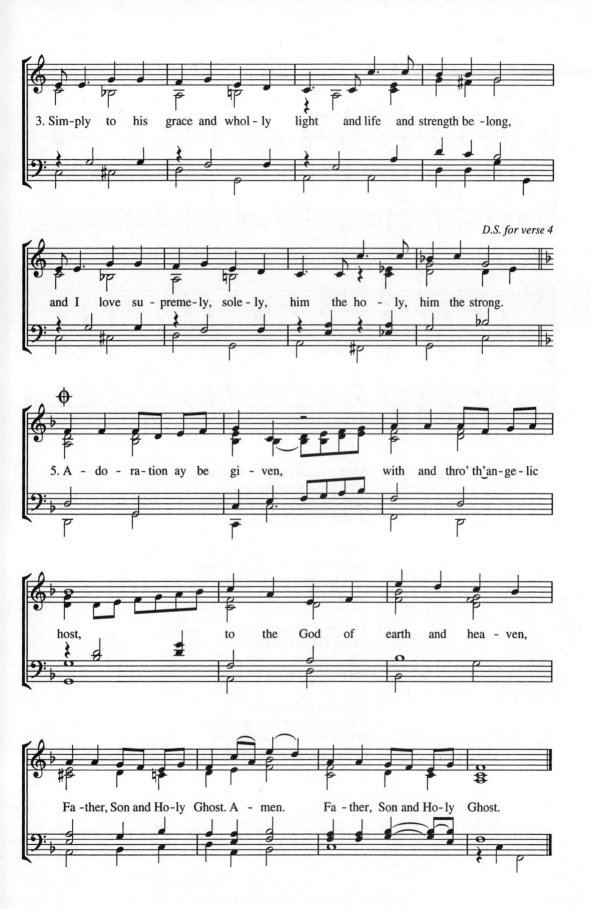

D.S. for verse 4

3. Sim-ply to his grace and whol-ly light and life and strength be -long,

and I love su - preme-ly, sole - ly, him the ho - ly, him the strong.

5. A - do - ra-tion ay be gi - ven, with and thro' th'an-ge-lic host, to the God of earth and hea - ven,

Fa -ther, Son and Ho-ly Ghost. A - men. Fa - ther, Son and Ho-ly Ghost.

John Henry Newman (1801-1890) alt.

Warwickshire ballad arr. and harm.
Ralph Vaughan Williams (1872-1958)

TUNE 2: SHIPSTON 87 87

1. Firm-ly I be-lieve and tru-ly God is Three and God is One;

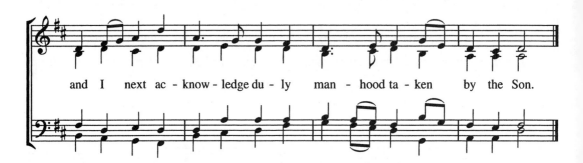

and I next ac-know-ledge du-ly man-hood ta-ken by the Son.

2. And I trust and hope most fully
   in the Saviour crucified;
   and each thought and deed unruly
   do to death as he has died.

3. Simply to his grace and wholly
   light and life and strength belong,
   and I love supremely, solely,
   him the holy, him the strong.

4. And I hold in veneration,
   for the love of him alone,
   holy Church as his creation,
   and her teachings as her own.

5. Adoration ay be given,
   with and through th' angelic host,
   to the God of earth and heaven,
   Father, Son and Holy Ghost.

75 For all the saints

William Walsham How (1823-1897)

Ralph Vaughan Williams (1872-1958)

SINE NOMINE 10 10 10 4

Unison

1. For all the saints who from their la-bours rest, who thee by faith be - fore the world con - fessed, thy name, O Je - sus, be for e - ver blest. Al - le - lu - ia, al - le - lu - ia!

2. Thou wast their rock, their fort - ress and their might; thou, Lord, their cap - tain in the well-fought fight; thou in the dark - ness drear their one true light. Al-

3. O may thy sol - diers, faith - ful, true and bold, fight as the saints who no - bly fought of old, and win, with them, the vic - tor's crown of gold.

Over to verses 4, 5, 6

Harmony

4. O blest com - mu - nion! fel - low - ship di - vine!
5. And when the strife is fierce, the war - fare long,
6. The gol - den eve - ning bright - ens in the west;

we fee - bly strug - gle, they in glo - ry shine; yet
steals on the ear the dis - tant tri - umph - song, and
soon, soon to faith - ful war - riors com - eth rest;

all are one in thee, for all are thine.
hearts are brave a - gain, and arms are strong. Al -
sweet is the calm of pa - ra - dise the blest.

al - le - lu - ia!

- le - lu - ia! al - le - lu - ia!

Unison

7. But lo! There breaks a yet more glo - rious day; the
8. From earth's wide bounds, from o - cean's far - thest coast, through

saints tri - um - phant rise in bright ar - ray: the
gates of pearl streams in the count-less host,

King of glo - ry pas - ses on his way. Al -
sing - ing to Fa - ther, Son and Ho - ly Ghost.

- le - lu - ia. al - le - lu - ia.

76 For the beauty of the earth

Folliot Sandford Pierpoint (1835-1917)

Geoffrey Shaw (1879-1943)
adapted from a folk song

ENGLAND'S LANE 77 77 77

1. For the beau-ty of the earth, for the beau-ty of the

skies, for the love which from our birth o - ver and a - round us

Refrain

lies: Lord of all, to thee we raise this our sac-ri-fice of praise.

2. For the beauty of each hour
of the day and of the night,
hill and vale and tree and flow'r,
sun and moon and stars of light:

3. For the joy of human love,
brother, sister, parent, child,
friends on earth, and friends above,
pleasures pure and undefiled:

4. For each perfect gift of thine,
to our race so freely giv'n,
graces human and divine,
flow'rs of earth and buds of heav'n:

5. For thy Church which evermore
lifteth holy hands above,
off'ring up on ev'ry shore
her pure sacrifice of love:

77 Forty days and forty nights

George Hunt Smyttan (1822-1870)
adapted by Michael Forster (b.1946)
AUS DER TIEFE (HEINLEIN) 77 77

Melody from
'Nürnbergisches Gesangbuch' (1676)

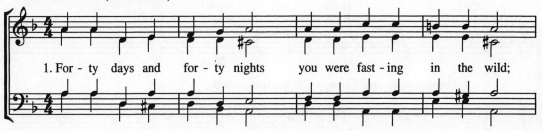

1. For-ty days and for-ty nights you were fast-ing in the wild;

for-ty days and for-ty nights, temp-ted still, yet un-be-guiled.

2. Sunbeams scorching all the day,
   chilly dew-drops nightly shed,
   prowling beasts about your way,
   stones your pillow, earth your bed.

3. Let us your endurance share,
   and from earthly greed abstain,
   with you vigilant in prayer,
   with you strong to suffer pain.

4. Then if evil on us press,
   flesh or spirit to assail,
   Victor in the wilderness,
   help us not to swerve or fail.

5. So shall peace divine be ours;
   holy gladness, pure and true:
   come to us, angelic powers,
   such as ministered to you.

6. Keep, O keep us, Saviour dear,
   ever constant by your side,
   that with you we may appear
   at th' eternal Eastertide.

78 From heaven you came

The Servant King

Graham Kendrick

Graham Kendrick (b.1950)

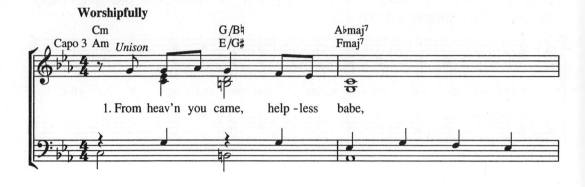

1. From heav'n you came, help-less babe,

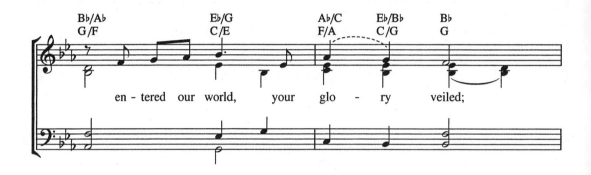

en-tered our world, your glo — ry veiled;

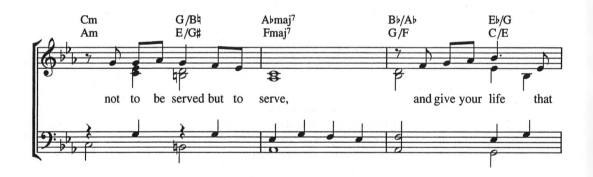

not to be served but to serve, and give your life that

we might live. *Refrain* This is our God, the Ser-vant

King, he calls us now to fol - low him, to bring our

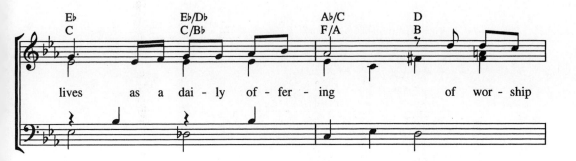

lives as a dai - ly of - fer - ing of wor - ship

to the Ser - vant King. King.

2. There in the garden of tears,
   my heavy load he chose to bear;
   his heart with sorrow was torn.
   'Yet not my will but yours,' he said.

3. Come see his hands and his feet,
   the scars that speak of sacrifice,
   hands that flung stars into space,
   to cruel nails surrendered.

4. So let us learn how to serve,
   and in our lives enthrone him;
   each other's needs to prefer,
   for it is Christ we're serving.

79 Give me joy in my heart

Sing hosanna

Traditional

Traditional arr. Colin Hand

1. Give me joy in my heart, keep me prais-ing, give me joy in my heart, I pray. Give me joy in my heart, keep me prais-ing, keep me prais-ing till the end of day. Sing ho-san-na! Sing ho-san-na! Sing ho-san-na to the King of kings! Sing ho-san-na! Sing ho-san-na! Sing ho-san-na to the King!

2. Give me peace in my heart, keep me resting,
   give me peace in my heart, I pray.
   Give me peace in my heart, keep me resting,
   keep me resting till the end of day.

3. Give me love in my heart, keep me serving,
   give me love in my heart, I pray.
   Give me love in my heart, keep me serving,
   keep me serving till the end of day.

4. Give me oil in my lamp, keep me burning,
   give me oil in my lamp, I pray.
   Give me oil in my lamp, keep me burning,
   keep me burning till the end of day.

80 Give thanks with a grateful heart

Henry Smith

Henry Smith

Give thanks with a grate-ful heart, give thanks to the Ho - ly One, give thanks be-cause he's gi-ven Je - sus Christ, his Son. And now let the weak say, 'I am strong', let the poor say, 'I am rich', be-cause of what the Lord has done for

us. And now let the weak say, 'I am

strong', let the poor say. 'I am rich', be-cause of

what the Lord has done for us.

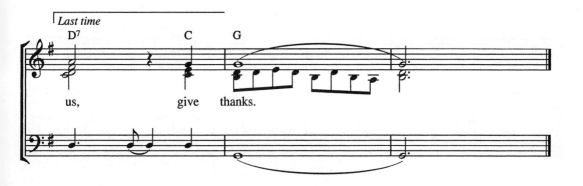

us, give thanks.

81 Glorious things of thee are spoken

John Newton (1725-1807)
based on Isaiah 33:20-21, alt.

Croatian folk melody adapted by
Franz Joseph Haydn (1732-1809)

AUSTRIA 87 87 D

1. Glo - rious things of thee are spo - ken, Zi - on, ci - ty of our God;

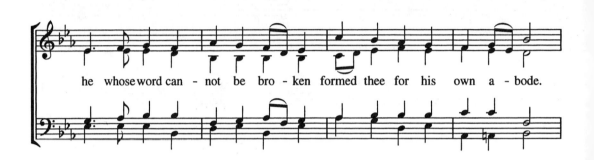

he whose word can - not be bro - ken formed thee for his own a - bode.

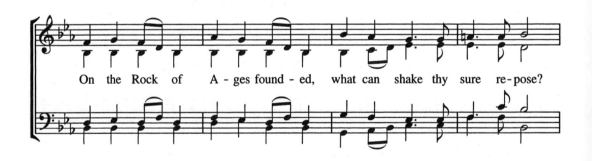

On the Rock of A - ges found - ed, what can shake thy sure re - pose?

With sal - va - tion's walls sur - round - ed, thou may'st smile at all thy foes.

2. See, the streams of living waters,
   springing from eternal love,
   well supply thy sons and daughters,
   and all fear of want remove.
   Who can faint while such a river
   ever flows their thirst to assuage?
   Grace which, like the Lord, the giver,
   never fails from age to age.

3. Round each habitation hov'ring,
   see the cloud and fire appear
   for a glory and a cov'ring,
   showing that the Lord is near.
   Thus they march, the pillar leading,
   light by night and shade by day;
   daily on the manna feeding
   which he gives them when they pray.

4. Saviour, if of Zion's city
   I through grace a member am,
   let the world deride or pity,
   I will glory in thy name.
   Fading is the worldling's pleasure,
   boasted pomp and empty show;
   solid joys and lasting treasure
   none but Zion's children know.

82 God be in my head

'Book of Hours' (1514)

Henry Walford Davies (1869-1941)

GOD BE IN MY HEAD Irregular

Organ

God be in my head, and in my un-der-stand-ing; God be in mine eyes, and in my look-ing; God be in my mouth, and in my speak-ing; God be in my heart, and in my think-ing; God be at mine end, and at my de-part-ing.

83 God is love: his the care

Percy Dearmer (1867-1936) alt.

From 'Piae Cantiones' (1582)
arr. Gustav Holst (1874-1934)

PERSONENT HODIE (THEODORIC) 666 66 and Refrain

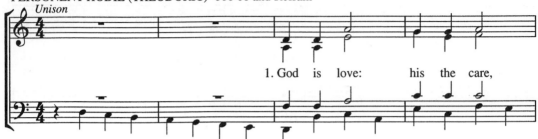

1. God is love: his the care,

tend - ing each, ev - 'ry-where. God is love, all is there!

Je - sus came to show him, that we all might know him!

Sing a - loud, loud, loud! Sing a - loud, loud, loud!

God is good! God is truth! God is beau-ty! Praise him!

2. None can see God above;
   we can share life and love;
   thus may we Godward move,
   seek him in creation,
   holding ev'ry nation.

3. Jesus lived on the earth,
   hope and life brought to birth
   and affirmed human worth,
   for he came to save us
   by the truth he gave us.

4. To our Lord praise we sing,
   light and life, friend and King,
   coming down, love to bring,
   pattern for our duty,
   showing God in beauty.

84 God moves in a mysterious way

William Cowper (1731-1800)

From the 'Scottish Psalter' (1635)
adapted by John Playford

LONDON NEW CM

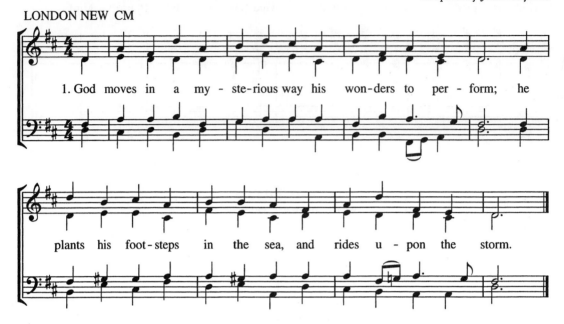

1. God moves in a my-ste-rious way his won-ders to per-form; he
plants his foot-steps in the sea, and rides u-pon the storm.

2. Deep in unfathomable mines
   of never-failing skill,
   he treasures up his bright designs,
   and works his sov'reign will.

3. Ye fearful saints, fresh courage take;
   the clouds ye so much dread
   are big with mercy, and shall break
   in blessings on your head.

4. Judge not the Lord by feeble sense,
   but trust him for his grace;
   behind a frowning providence
   he hides a shining face.

5. His purposes will ripen fast,
   unfolding ev'ry hour;
   the bud may have a bitter taste,
   but sweet will be the flow'r.

6. Blind unbelief is sure to err,
   and scan his work in vain;
   God is his own interpreter,
   and he will make it plain.

85 God of mercy, God of grace

Henry Francis Lyte (1793-1847)
based on Psalm 67, alt.

Henry Smart (1813-1879)

HEATHLANDS 77 77 77

1. God of mer - cy, God of grace, show the bright-ness of thy face;
shine u - pon us, Sa - viour, shine, fill thy Church with light di - vine;
and thy sav - ing health ex - tend un - to earth's re - mo - test end.

2. Let the people praise thee, Lord;
   be by all that live adored;
   let the nations shout and sing
   glory to their Saviour King;
   at thy feet their tribute pay,
   and thy holy will obey.

3. Let the people praise thee, Lord;
   earth shall then her fruits afford;
   God to us his blessing give,
   we to God devoted live;
   all below, and all above,
   one in joy and light and love.

86 God's Spirit is in my heart

Go, tell everyone

Alan Dale
Hubert J. Richards

Hubert J. Richards (b.1921)
arr. Keith Stent

1. God's Spi - rit is in my heart. He has called me and set me a -

part. This is what I have to do, what I have to

do. He sent me to give the Good News to the

poor, tell pris -'ners that they are pris -'ners no more, tell

blind peo - ple that they can see, and set the

2. Just as the Father sent me,
   so I'm sending you out to be
   my witnesses throughout the world,
   the whole of the world.

3. Don't carry a load in your pack,
   you don't need two shirts on your back.
   A workman can earn his own keep,
   can earn his own keep.

4. Don't worry what you have to say,
   don't worry because on that day
   God's Spirit will speak in your heart,
   will speak in your heart.

87 Go forth and tell

James Edward Seddon (1915-1983)

John Barnard (b.1948)

YANWORTH 10 10 10 10

Unison

1. Go forth and tell! O Church of God, a-wake! God's

sav - ing news to all the na - tions take:

pro - claim Christ Je - sus, Sa - viour, Lord and King,

that all the world his wor - thy praise may sing.

2. Go forth and tell! God's love embraces all;
   he will in grace respond to all who call;
   how shall they call if they have never heard
   the gracious invitation of his word?

3. Go forth and tell! where still the darkness lies;
   in wealth or want, the sinner surely dies:
   give us, O Lord, concern of heart and mind,
   a love like yours which cares for all mankind.

4. Go forth and tell! the doors are open wide:
   share God's good gifts – let no-one be denied;
   live out your life as Christ your Lord shall choose,
   your ransomed pow'rs for his sole glory use.

5. Go forth and tell! O Church of God, arise!
   Go in the strength which Christ your Lord supplies;
   go till all nations his great name adore
   and serve him, Lord and King, for evermore.

88 Good King Wenceslas

John Mason Neale (1818-1866) alt.

'Piae Cantiones' (1582)
arr. John Stainer

TEMPUS ADEST FLORIDUM 76 76 D

1. Good King Wen-ces - las looked out on the feast of Ste - phen, when the snow lay round a-bout, deep, and crisp, and e - ven; bright-ly shone the moon that night, though the frost was cru - el, when a poor man came in sight, gath-'ring win - ter fu - el.

2. 'Hither, page, and stand by me,
   if thou know'st it, telling,
   yonder peasant, who is he,
   where and what his dwelling?'
   'Sire, he lives a good league hence,
   underneath the mountain,
   right against the forest fence,
   by Saint Agnes' fountain.'

3. 'Bring me flesh, and bring me wine,
   bring me pine logs hither:
   thou and I will see him dine,
   when we bring them thither.'
   Page and monarch, forth they went,
   forth they went together;
   through the rude wind's wild lament,
   and the bitter weather.

4. 'Sire, the night is darker now,
   and the wind blows stronger;
   fails my heart, I know not how;
   I can go no longer.'
   'Mark my footsteps good, my page;
   tread thou in them boldly:
   thou shalt find the winter's rage
   freeze thy blood less coldly.'

5. In his master's steps he trod,
   where the snow lay dinted;
   heat was in the very sod
   which the Saint had printed.
   Therefore, Christians all, be sure,
   wealth or rank possessing,
   ye who now will bless the poor,
   shall yourselves find blessing.

89 Great is thy faithfulness

Thomas Obadiah Chilsholm (1866-1960)

William Marion Runyan (1870-1957)

FAITHFULNESS (RUNYAN) 11 10 11 10 and Refrain

1. Great is thy faith - ful - ness, O God, my Fa - ther,

there is no sha - dow of turn - ing with thee;

thou chang - est not, thy com - pas - sions, they fail not;

as thou hast been thou for e - ver wilt be.

Refrain

Great is thy faith - ful - ness! Great is thy faith - ful - ness!

Morn - ing by morn - ing new mer - cies I see;
all I have need - ed thy hand hath pro - vi - ded,
great is thy faith - ful - ness, Lord, un - to me!

2. Summer and winter, and springtime and harvest,
   sun, moon and stars in their courses above,
   join with all nature in manifold witness
   to thy great faithfulness, mercy and love.

3. Pardon for sin and a peace that endureth,
   thine own dear presence to cheer and to guide;
   strength for today and bright hope for tomorrow,
   blessings all mine, with ten thousand beside!

90 Guide me, O thou great Redeemer

William Williams (1717-1791)
trans. Peter Williams (1727-1796) and others

John Hughes (1873-1932)

CWM RHONDDA 87 87 47

1. Guide me, O thou great Re-deem-er, pil-grim through this bar-ren land; I am weak, but thou art migh-ty, hold me with thy pow'r-ful hand: Bread of Hea-ven, Bread of Hea-ven, feed me till I want no more, (want no more,) feed me till I want no more. (want no more,)

2. Open now the crystal fountain,
   whence the healing stream doth flow;
   let the fire and cloudy pillar
   lead me all my journey through;
   strong deliv'rer, strong deliv'rer,
   be thou still my strength and shield,
   be thou still my strength and shield.

3. When I tread the verge of Jordan,
   bid my anxious fears subside;
   death of death, and hell's destruction,
   land me safe on Canaan's side;
   songs of praises, songs of praises,
   I will ever give to thee,
   I will ever give to thee.

91 Hail the day that sees him rise

Charles Wesley (1707-1788),
Thomas Cotterill (1779-1823)
and others, alt.

Robert Williams (1781-1821)

LLANFAIR 77 77 and Alleluias

1. Hail the day that sees him rise, al - le - lu - ia!

to his throne a - bove the skies; al - le - lu - ia!

Christ the Lamb, for sin - ners giv'n, al - le - lu - ia!

en - ters now the high - est heav'n! al - le - lu - ia!

2. There for him high triumph waits;
   lift your heads, eternal gates!
   He hath conquered death and sin;
   take the King of Glory in!

3. Circled round with angel-pow'rs,
   their triumphant Lord and ours;
   wide unfold the radiant scene,
   take the King of Glory in!

4. Lo, the heav'n its Lord receives,
   yet he loves the earth he leaves;
   though returning to his throne,
   calls the human race his own.

5. See, he lifts his hands above;
   see, he shows the prints of love;
   hark, his gracious lips bestow
   blessings on his Church below.

6. Still for us he intercedes,
   his prevailing death he pleads;
   near himself prepares our place,
   he the first-fruits of our race.

7. Lord, though parted from our sight,
   far above the starry height,
   grant our hearts may thither rise,
   seeking thee above the skies.

8. Ever upward let us move,
   wafted on the wings of love;
   looking when our Lord shall come,
   longing, sighing after home.

92 Hail to the Lord's anointed

Paraphrase of Psalm 72
by James Montgomery (1771-1854)

From a melody in Johann Crüger's 'Gesangbuch'
adapted by William Henry Monk (1823-1889)

CRÜGER 76 76 D

1. Hail to the Lord's a - noint - ed, great Da - vid's great - er son! Hail, in the time ap - point - ed, his reign on earth be - gun! He comes to break op - pres - sion, to set the cap - tive free; to take a - way trans - gres - sion, and rule in e - qui - ty.

2. He comes with succour speedy
to those who suffer wrong;
to help the poor and needy,
and bid the weak be strong;
to give them songs for sighing,
their darkness turn to light,
whose souls, condemned and dying,
were precious in his sight.

3. He shall come down like showers
upon the fruitful earth,
and love, joy, hope, like flowers,
spring in his path to birth:
before him on the mountains
shall peace the herald go;
and righteousness in fountains
from hill to valley flow.

4. Kings shall fall down before him,
and gold and incense bring;
all nations shall adore him,
his praise all people sing;
to him shall prayer unceasing
and daily vows ascend;
his kingdom still increasing,
a kingdom without end.

5. O'er ev'ry foe victorious,
he on his throne shall rest,
from age to age more glorious,
all-blessing and all-blest;
the tide of time shall never
his covenant remove;
his name shall stand for ever;
that name to us is love.

93 Hallelujah, my Father

Tim Cullen, alt.

Tim Cullen

Unison

Hal-le-lu-jah, my Fa-ther, for giv-ing us your

Son; send-ing him in-to the world to be giv-en up for

all, know-ing we would bruise him and smite him from the

earth! Hal-le-lu-jah, my Fa-ther, in his

death   is   my   birth.   Hal - le - lu - jah,   my

Fa - ther,   in his life   is   my   life.

94 Hark! a herald voice is calling

'Vox clara ecce intonat' (6th century)
trans. Edward Caswall (1814-1878)

William Henry Monk (1823-1889)

MERTON 87 87

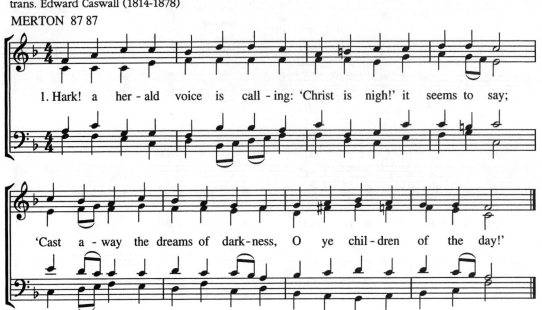

1. Hark! a her - ald voice is call - ing: 'Christ is nigh!' it seems to say;
'Cast a - way the dreams of dark-ness, O ye chil - dren of the day!'

2. Startled at the solemn warning,
   let the earth-bound soul arise;
   Christ, her sun, all sloth dispelling,
   shines upon the morning skies.

3. Lo, the Lamb, so long expected,
   comes with pardon down from heav'n;
   let us haste, with tears of sorrow,
   one and all to be forgiv'n.

4. So when next he comes with glory,
   wrapping all the earth in fear,
   may he then, as our defender,
   on the clouds of heav'n appear.

5. Honour, glory, virtue, merit,
   to the Father and the Son,
   with the co-eternal Spirit,
   while unending ages run.

95 Hark, the glad sound!

Philip Doddridge (1702-1751)
based on Luke 4:18-19

Thomas Ravenscroft (c.1582-c.1633),
'Psalms' (1621)

BRISTOL CM

1. Hark, the glad sound! the Sa - viour comes, the Sa - viour pro - mised long: let ev - 'ry heart pre - pare a throne, and ev - 'ry voice a song.

2. He comes, the pris'ners to release
   in Satan's bondage held;
   the gates of brass before him burst,
   the iron fetters yield.

3. He comes, the broken heart to bind,
   the bleeding soul to cure,
   and with the treasures of his grace
   to bless the humble poor.

4. Our glad hosannas, Prince of Peace,
   thy welcome shall proclaim;
   and heav'n's eternal arches ring
   with thy belovèd name.

96 Hark, the herald-angels sing

Charles Wesley (1707-1788),
George Whitefield (1714-1770),
Martin Madan (1726-1790) and others, alt.

Adapted from Felix Mendelssohn (1809-1847)
by William Hayman Cummings (1831-1915)

MENDELSSOHN 77 77 D and Refrain

1. Hark, the he - rald - an - gels sing glo - ry to the new-born King; peace on earth and mer-cy mild, God and sin - ners re-con - ciled: joy-ful, all ye na - tions rise, join the tri-umph of the skies, with th'an - ge - lic host pro - claim, 'Christ is born in Beth - le - hem.'

Refrain

Unison

Hark, the her - ald - an - gels sing glo - ry to the new-born King.

Ped.

2. Christ, by highest heav'n adored,
   Christ, the everlasting Lord,
   late in time behold him come,
   offspring of a virgin's womb!
   Veiled in flesh the Godhead see,
   hail, th'incarnate Deity!
   Pleased as man with us to dwell,
   Jesus, our Emmanuel.

3. Hail, the heav'n-born Prince of Peace!
   Hail, the Sun of Righteousness!
   Light and life to all he brings,
   ris'n with healing in his wings;
   mild he lays his glory by,
   born that we no more may die,
   born to raise us from the earth,
   born to give us second birth.

97 He who would valiant be

Percy Dearmer (1867-1936)
after John Bunyan (1628-1688)

Traditional English melody collected and
arr. Ralph Vaughan Williams (1872-1958)

MONKS GATE 65 65 66 65

1. He who would val-iant be 'gainst all dis-as-ter,
let him in con-stan-cy fol - low the Mas-ter.
There's no dis-cour-age - ment shall make him once re -
lent his first a-vowed in - tent to be a pil-grim.

2. Who so beset him round
with dismal stories,
do but themselves confound –
his strength the more is.
No foes shall stay his might,
though he with giants fight:
he will make good his right
to be a pilgrim.

3. Since, Lord, thou dost defend
us with thy Spirit,
we know we at the end
shall life inherit.
Then fancies flee away!
I'll fear not what men say,
I'll labour night and day
to be a pilgrim.

98 Hills of the north, rejoice

Charles Edward Oakley (1832-1865), adapted

Martin Shaw (1875-1958)

LITTLE CORNARD 66 66 88

1. Hills of the north, re-joice, e-cho-ing songs a-rise, hail with u-ni-ted voice him who made earth and skies: he comes in right-eous-ness and love, he brings sal-va-tion from a-bove.

2. Isles of the southern seas
sing to the list'ning earth,
carry on ev'ry breeze
hope of a world's new birth:
in Christ shall all be made anew,
his word is sure, his promise true.

3. Lands of the east, arise,
he is your brightest morn,
greet him with joyous eyes,
praise shall his path adorn:
the God whom you have longed to know
in Christ draws near, and calls you now.

4. Shores of the utmost west,
lands of the setting sun,
welcome the heav'nly guest
in whom the dawn has come:
he brings a never-ending light
who triumphed o'er our darkest night.

5. Shout, as you journey on,
songs be in ev'ry mouth,
lo, from the north they come,
from east and west and south:
in Jesus all shall find their rest,
in him the longing earth be blest.

99 Holy, holy, holy! Lord God almighty

Reginald Heber (1783-1826)

John Bacchus Dykes (1823-1876)

NICAEA 11 12 12 10

1. Ho-ly, ho-ly, ho-ly! Lord God al-migh-ty!
Ear-ly in the morn-ing our song shall rise to thee;
ho-ly, ho-ly, ho-ly! Mer-ci-ful and migh-ty!
God in three per-sons, bles-sed Tri-ni-ty!

* 2. Holy, holy, holy! All the saints adore thee,
    casting down their golden crowns around the glassy sea;
    cherubim and seraphim falling down before thee,
    which wert, and art, and evermore shall be.

3. Holy, holy, holy! Though the darkness hide thee,
    though the eye made blind by sin thy glory may not see,
    only thou art holy, there is none beside thee,
    perfect in pow'r, in love, and purity.

4. Holy, holy, holy! Lord God almighty!
    All thy works shall praise thy name, in earth, and sky and sea;
    holy, holy, holy! Merciful and mighty!
    God in three persons, blessèd Trinity!

* *May be omitted*

100 Hosanna, hosanna

Carl Tuttle

Carl Tuttle

Lively

Unison

1. Ho - san - na, ho - san - na, ho - san - na in the high - est! Ho - san - na, ho - san - na, ho - san - na in the high - est!

Refrain

Lord, we lift up your name, with hearts full of praise; be ex - al - ted, O Lord, my God! Ho - san - na in the high - est!

2. Glory, glory, glory to the King of kings!
Glory, glory, glory to the King of kings!

101 How deep the Father's love for us

Stuart Townend

Stuart Townend

1. How deep the Fa - ther's love for us, how vast be-yond all mea - sure, that he should give his on - ly Son to make a wretch his trea - sure. How great the pain of sear - ing loss, the Fa - ther turns his face a - way, as wounds which mar the Cho - sen One bring

ma - ny sons to glo - ry.

2. Behold the man upon a cross,
   my sin upon his shoulders;
   ashamed, I hear my mocking voice
   call out among the scoffers.
   It was my sin that held him there
   until it was accomplished;
   his dying breath has brought me life –
   I know that it is finished.

3. I will not boast in anything,
   no gifts, no pow'r, no wisdom;
   but I will boast in Jesus Christ,
   his death and resurrection.
   Why should I gain from his reward?
   I cannot give an answer,
   but this I know with all my heart,
   his wounds have paid my ransom.

102 How firm a foundation

Richard Keen (c.1787)   'Magdalen Hospital Hymns' (c.1760)

MONTGOMERY 11 11 11 11

1. How firm a foun-da-tion, ye saints of the Lord, is laid for your
faith in his ex-cel-lent word; what more can he say than to
you he hath said, you who un-to Je-sus for re-fuge have fled?

2. Fear not, he is with thee, O be not dismayed;
   for he is thy God, and will still give thee aid:
   he'll strengthen thee, help thee, and cause thee to stand,
   upheld by his righteous, omnipotent hand.

3. In ev'ry condition, in sickness, in health,
   in poverty's vale, or abounding in wealth;
   at home and abroad, on the land, on the sea,
   as thy days may demand shall thy strength ever be.

4. When through the deep waters he calls thee to go,
   the rivers of grief shall not thee overflow;
   for he will be with thee in trouble to bless,
   and sanctify to thee thy deepest distress.

5. When through fiery trials thy pathway shall lie,
   his grace all-sufficient shall be thy supply;
   the flame shall not hurt thee, his only design
   thy dross to consume and thy gold to refine.

6. The soul that on Jesus has leaned for repose
   he will not, he cannot, desert to its foes;
   that soul, though all hell should endeavour to shake,
   he never will leave, he will never forsake.

103 How lovely on the mountains

Our God reigns

v.1 Leonard E. Smith Jnr.
based on Isaiah 52:7
vs. 2-4 unknown

Leonard E. Smith Jnr. (b.1942)
arr. Keith Stent

our God reigns,   our God reigns.

2. You watchmen, lift your voices
   joyfully as one,
   shout for your King, your King!
   See eye to eye,
   the Lord restoring Zion:
   our God reigns, our God reigns.

3. Wasteplaces of Jerusalem,
   break forth with joy!
   We are redeemed, redeemed.
   The Lord has saved
   and comforted his people:
   our God reigns, our God reigns.

4. Ends of the earth, see
   the salvation of our God!
   Jesus is Lord, is Lord!
   Before the nations,
   he has bared his holy arm:
   our God reigns, our God reigns.

104 How sweet the name of Jesus sounds

John Newton (1725-1807)   Alexander Robert Reinagle (1799-1877)

ST PETER CM

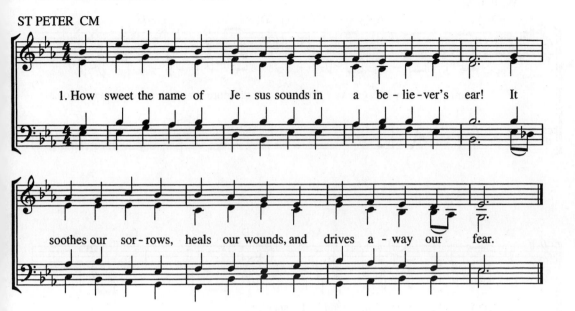

1. How sweet the name of Je-sus sounds in a be-lie-ver's ear! It soothes our sor-rows, heals our wounds, and drives a-way our fear.

2. It makes the wounded spirit whole,
   and calms the troubled breast;
   'tis manna to the hungry soul,
   and to the weary, rest.

3. Dear name! the rock on which I build,
   my shield and hiding-place,
   my never-failing treas'ry filled
   with boundless stores of grace.

4. Jesus! my shepherd, brother, friend,
   my prophet, priest, and king,
   my Lord, my life, my way, my end,
   accept the praise I bring.

5. Weak is the effort of my heart,
   and cold my warmest thought;
   but when I see thee as thou art,
   I'll praise thee as I ought.

6. Till then I would thy love proclaim
   with ev'ry fleeting breath;
   and may the music of thy name
   refresh my soul in death.

105 I am a new creation

Dave Bilbrough   Dave Bilbrough

With drive

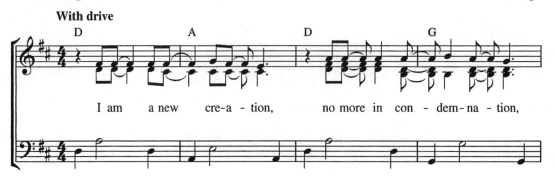

I am a new cre-a-tion, no more in con-dem-na-tion,

here in the grace of God I stand.

My heart is o-ver-flow-ing, my love just keeps on grow-ing,

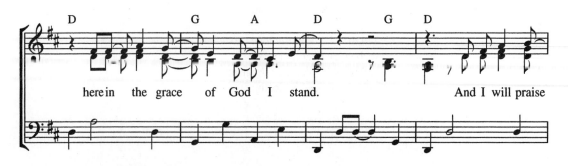

here in the grace of God I stand. And I will praise

you, Lord,   yes, I will praise   you, Lord,

and I will sing   of all   that you have done.

A joy   that knows   no lim - it,   a light -ness in

my spi - rit,   here in   the   grace   of   God   I   stand.

1.

2.

106 I cannot tell

William Young Fullerton (1857-1932) alt.

Traditional Irish melody
arr. Noel Rawsthorne

LONDONDERRY AIR 11 10 11 10 11 10 11 12

Unison

1. I can-not tell how he whom an-gels wor - ship should stoop to love the peo - ples of the earth, or why as shep - herd he should seek the wand - 'rer with his mys - te - rious pro-mise of new birth. But this I know, that he was born of Ma - ry, when Beth-l'em's man - ger was his on - ly

home,   and that he lived   at Na - za - reth and

la - boured,   and so the   Sa-viour, Sa-viour of the world, is come.

2. I cannot tell how silently he suffered,
    as with his peace he graced this place of tears,
    or how his heart upon the cross was broken,
    the crown of pain to three and thirty years.
    But this I know, he heals the broken-hearted,
    and stays our sin, and calms our lurking fear,
    and lifts the burden from the heavy laden,
    for yet the Saviour, Saviour of the world, is here.

3. I cannot tell how he will win the nations,
    how he will claim his earthly heritage,
    how satisfy the needs and aspirations
    of east and west, of sinner and of sage.
    But this I know, all flesh shall see his glory,
    and he shall reap the harvest he has sown,
    and some glad day his sun shall shine in splendour
    when he the Saviour, Saviour of the world, is known.

4. I cannot tell how all the lands shall worship,
    when, at his bidding, ev'ry storm is stilled,
    or who can say how great the jubilation
    when ev'ry heart with perfect love is filled.
    But this I know, the skies will thrill with rapture,
    and myriad, myriad human voices sing,
    and earth to heav'n and heav'n to earth, will answer:
    'At last the Saviour, Saviour of the world, is King!'

107 I danced in the morning

Lord of the dance

Sydney Carter

Traditional American melody
adapted by Sydney Carter (b.1915)
arr. Noel Rawsthorne

1. I danced in the mor-ning when the world was be-gun, and I danced in the moon and the stars and the sun, and I came down from hea-ven and I danced on the earth, at Beth-le-hem I had my birth.

Refrain

Dance, then, wher-e-ver you may be, I am the Lord of the

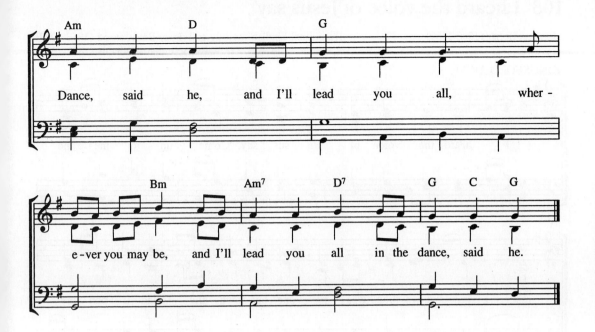

Dance, said he, and I'll lead you all, wher-
e-ver you may be, and I'll lead you all in the dance, said he.

2. I danced for the scribe and the Pharisee,
   but they would not dance and they wouldn't follow me.
   I danced for the fishermen, for James and John –
   they came with me and the dance went on.

3. I danced on the Sabbath and I cured the lame;
   the holy people, they said it was a shame.
   They whipped and they stripped and they hung me on high,
   and they left me there on a cross to die.

4. I danced on a Friday when the sky turned black –
   it's hard to dance with the devil on your back.
   They buried my body, and they thought I'd gone,
   but I am the dance, and I still go on.

5. They cut me down and I leapt up high;
   I am the life that'll never, never die;
   I'll live in you if you'll live in me –
   I am the Lord of the Dance, said he.

108 I heard the voice of Jesus say

Horatius Bonar (1808-1889)

Traditional English melody coll. Lucy Broadwood (1858-1929)
arr. Ralph Vaughan Williams (1872-1958)

KINGSFOLD DCM

1. I heard the voice of Je-sus say, 'Come un-to me and rest; lay down, thou wea-ry one, lay down thy head u-pon my breast.' I came to Je-sus as I was, so wea-ry, worn and sad; I found in him a rest-ing-place, and he has made me glad.

2. I heard the voice of Jesus say,
   'Behold, I freely give
   the living water, thirsty one;
   stoop down and drink and live.'
   I came to Jesus, and I drank
   of that life-giving stream;
   my thirst was quenched, my soul revived,
   and now I live in him.

3. I heard the voice of Jesus say,
   'I am this dark world's light;
   look unto me, thy morn shall rise,
   and all thy day be bright.'
   I looked to Jesus, and I found
   in him my star, my sun;
   and in that light of life I'll walk
   till trav'lling days are done.

109 Immortal, invisible, God only wise

Walter Chalmers Smith (1824-1908)
based on 1 Timothy1:17

Adapted from a traditional Welsh hymn melody
in John Roberts' 'Caniadu y Cyssegr' (1839)

ST DENIO 11 11 11 11

1. Im - mor - tal, in - vis - i - ble, God on - ly wise, in
light in - ac - ces - si - ble hid from our eyes, most
bless - ed, most glo - rious, the An - cient of Days, al -
migh - ty, vic - to - rious, thy great name we praise.

2. Unresting, unhasting, and silent as light,
   nor wanting, nor wasting, thou rulest in might;
   thy justice like mountains high soaring above
   thy clouds which are fountains of goodness and love.

3. To all life thou givest, to both great and small;
   in all life thou livest, the true life of all;
   we blossom and flourish as leaves on the tree,
   and wither and perish; but naught changeth thee.

4. Great Father of glory, pure Father of light,
   thine angels adore thee, all veiling their sight;
   all laud we would render, O help us to see
   'tis only the splendour of light hideth thee.

110 Immortal love, for ever full

John Greenleaf Whittier (1807-1892)

Probably by Jeremiah Clarke (c.1674-1707)

BISHOPTHORPE CM

1. Immortal love, for ever full, for ever flowing free, for ever shared, for ever whole, a never-ebbing sea.

2. Our outward lips confess the name
   all other names above;
   love only knoweth whence it came
   and comprehendeth love.

3. O warm, sweet, tender, even yet
   a present help is he;
   and faith has still its Olivet,
   and love its Galilee.

4. The healing of his seamless dress
   is by our beds of pain;
   we touch him in life's throng and press,
   and we are whole again.

5. Through him the first fond prayers are said
   our lips of childhood frame;
   the last low whispers of our dead
   are burdened with his name.

6. Alone, O love ineffable,
   thy saving name is giv'n;
   to turn aside from thee is hell,
   to walk with thee is heav'n.

111 In heavenly love abiding

Anna Laetitia Waring (1820-1910)
based on Psalm 23

David Jenkins (1848-1915)

PENLAN 76 76 D

1. In heav'n-ly love a-bi-ding, no change my heart shall

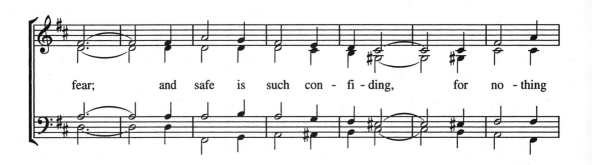

fear; and safe is such con-fi-ding, for no-thing

chan-ges here. The storm may roar with-out me, my

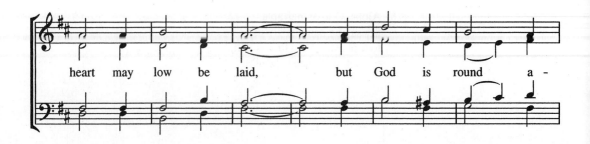

heart may low be laid, but God is round a-

bout me,   and   can   I   be   dis - mayed?

2. Wherever he may guide me,
   no want shall turn me back;
   my Shepherd is beside me,
   and nothing shall I lack.
   His wisdom ever waketh,
   his sight is never dim,
   he knows the way he taketh,
   and I will walk with him.

3. Green pastures are before me,
   which yet I have not seen;
   bright skies will soon be o'er me,
   where the dark clouds have been.
   My hope I cannot measure,
   my path to life is free,
   my Saviour has my treasure,
   and he will walk with me.

112 In the bleak mid-winter

Christina Georgina Rossetti (1830-1894)   Gustav Holst (1874-1934)

CRANHAM Irregular

1. In the bleak mid - win - ter fros - ty wind made
2. Our God, heav'n can - not hold him nor earth sus -
3. E - nough for him, whom che - ru - bim wor - ship night and
4. An - gels and arch - an - gels may have ga - thered
5. What can I give him, poor as I

moan, earth stood hard as ir - on, wa - ter like a
tain; heav'n and earth shall flee a - way when he comes to
day, a breast - ful of milk, and a man - ger - ful of
there, che - ru - bim and se - ra - phim thronged the
am? If I were a shep - herd I would bring a

stone; snow had fal - len, snow on snow, snow on
reign. In the bleak mid - win - ter a sta - ble - place suf -
hay: e - nough for him, whom an - gels fall down be -
air; but on - ly his mo - ther in her mai - den
lamb; if I were a wise man I would do my

snow, in the bleak mid - win - ter, long a - go.
fleed the Lord God al - migh - ty, Je - sus Christ.
fore, the ox and ass and ca - mel which a - dore.
bliss wor - shipped the be - lov - ed with a kiss.
part, yet what I can I give him: give my heart.

113 It came upon the midnight clear

Edmund Hamilton Sears (1810-1876) alt.

Traditional English melody
arr. Arthur Seymour Sullivan

NOEL DCM

1. It came up-on the mid-night clear, that glo-rious song of old, from an-gels bend-ing near the earth to touch their harps of gold: 'Peace on the earth, good-will to all, from heav'n's all-gra-cious King!' The world in so-lemn still-ness lay to hear the an-gels sing.

2. Still through the cloven skies they come,
with peaceful wings unfurled;
and still their heav'nly music floats
o'er all the weary world:
above its sad and lowly plains
they bend on hov'ring wing;
and ever o'er its Babel-sounds
the blessèd angels sing.

3. Yet with the woes of sin and strife
the world has suffered long;
beneath the angel-strain have rolled
two thousand years of wrong;
and warring humankind hears not
the love-song which they bring:
O hush the noise of mortal strife,
and hear the angels sing!

4. And ye, beneath life's crushing load,
whose forms are bending low,
who toil along the climbing way
with painful steps and slow:
look now! for glad and golden hours
come swiftly on the wing;
O rest beside the weary road,
and hear the angels sing.

5. For lo, the days are hast'ning on,
by prophets seen of old,
when with the ever-circling years
comes round the age of gold;
when peace shall over all the earth
its ancient splendours fling,
and all the world give back the song
which now the angels sing.

114 I, the Lord of sea and sky

Here I am, Lord

Dan Schutte based on Isaiah 6

Dan Schutte

HERE I AM 77 74 D and Refrain

1. I, the Lord of sea and sky, I have heard my peo-ple cry.

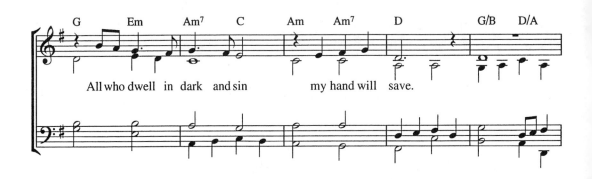

All who dwell in dark and sin my hand will save.

I, who made the stars of night, I will make their dark-ness bright.

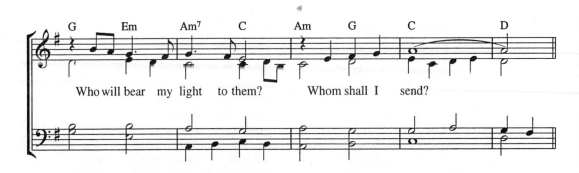

Who will bear my light to them? Whom shall I send?

2. I, the Lord of snow and rain,
   I have borne my people's pain.
   I have wept for love of them.
   They turn away.
   I will break their hearts of stone,
   give them hearts for love alone.
   I will speak my word to them.
   Whom shall I send?

3. I, the Lord of wind and flame,
   I will tend the poor and lame.
   I will set a feast for them.
   My hand will save.
   Finest bread I will provide
   till their hearts be satisfied.
   I will give my life to them.
   Whom shall I send?

115 It is a thing most wonderful

William Walsham How (1823-1897)

Traditional English melody collected and
arr. Ralph Vaughan Williams (1872-1958)

HERONGATE LM

1. It is a thing most won - der - ful, al - most too won - der - ful to be, that God's own Son should come from heav'n, and die to save a child like me.

2. And yet I know that it is true:
   he chose a poor and humble lot,
   and wept and toiled, and mourned and died,
   for love of those who loved him not.

3. I cannot tell how he could love
   a child so weak and full of sin;
   his love must be most wonderful,
   if he could die my love to win.

4. I sometimes think about the cross,
   and shut my eyes, and try to see
   the cruel nails and crown of thorns,
   and Jesus crucified for me.

5. But even could I see him die,
   I could but see a little part
   of that great love which, like a fire,
   is always burning in his heart.

6. It is most wonderful to know
   his love for me so free and sure;
   but 'tis more wonderful to see
   my love for him so faint and poor.

7. And yet I want to love thee, Lord;
   O light the flame within my heart,
   and I will love thee more and more,
   until I see thee as thou art.

116 I will enter his gates

He has made me glad

Leona von Brethorst

Leona von Brethorst

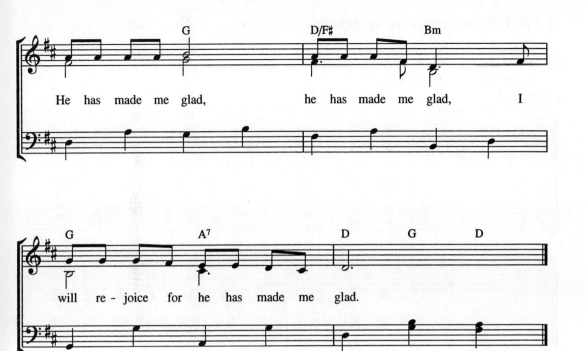

117 Jerusalem the golden

From 'De Contemptu Mundi'
by St Bernard of Cluny (12th century)
trans. John Mason Neale (1818-1866) alt.

Alexander Ewing (1830-1895)

EWING 76 76 D

1. Jerusalem the golden, with milk and honey blest, beneath thy contemplation sink heart and voice oppressed. I know not, ah, I know not what joys await us there, what radiancy of glory, what bliss beyond compare.

2. They stand, those halls of Zion,
all jubilant with song,
and bright with many angels,
and all the martyr throng;
the prince is ever with them,
the daylight is serene;
the pastures of the blessèd
are decked in glorious sheen.

3. There is the throne of David;
and there, from care released,
the shout of them that triumph,
the song of them that feast;
and they, who with their leader
have fully run the race,
are robed in white for ever
before their Saviour's face.

4. O sweet and blessèd country,
the home of God's elect!
O sweet and blessèd country
that eager hearts expect!
Jesus, in mercy, bring us
to that dear land of rest;
who art, with God the Father
and Spirit, ever blest.

118 Jesu, lover of my soul

Charles Wesley (1707-1788) alt.

Joseph Parry (1841-1903)

ABERYSTWYTH 77 77 D

1. Je-su, lo-ver of my soul, let me to thy bo-som fly,
while the gath-'ring wa-ters roll, while the tem-pest still is high:
hide me, O my Sa-viour, hide, till the storm of life is past;
safe in-to the ha-ven guide, O re-ceive my soul at last.

2. Other refuge have I none,
hangs my helpless soul on thee;
leave, ah, leave me not alone,
still support and comfort me.
All my trust on thee is stayed,
all my help from thee I bring;
cover my defenceless head
with the shadow of thy wing.

3. Plenteous grace with thee is found,
grace to cleanse from ev'ry sin;
let the healing streams abound,
make and keep me pure within.
Thou of life the fountain art,
freely let me take of thee,
spring thou up within my heart,
rise to all eternity.

119 Jesus calls us: o'er the tumult

Cecil Frances Alexander (1818-1895)   Edward Henry Thorne (1834-1916)

ST ANDREW 87 87

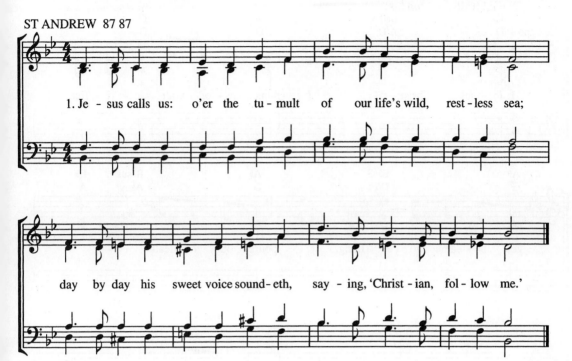

1. Je - sus calls us: o'er the tu - mult of our life's wild, rest - less sea;

day by day his sweet voice sound- eth, say - ing, 'Christ - ian, fol - low me.'

2. As of old Saint Andrew heard it
   by the Galilean lake,
   turned from home and toil and kindred,
   leaving all for his dear sake.

3. Jesus calls us from the worship
   of the vain world's golden store,
   from each idol that would keep us,
   saying, 'Christian, love me more.'

4. In our joys and in our sorrows,
   days of toil and hours of ease,
   still he calls, in cares and pleasures,
   that we love him more than these.

5. Jesus calls us: by thy mercies,
   Saviour, make us hear thy call,
   give our hearts to thine obedience,
   serve and love thee best of all.

120 Jesus Christ

Once again

Matt Redman

Matt Redman

Thoughtfully, not too fast

1. Je - sus Christ, I think up - on your sac - ri - fice;
you be - came no - thing, poured out to death.
Ma - ny times I've won-dered at your gift of life, and
I'm in that place once a-gain, I'm in that place once a-gain.
And once a - gain I look up - on the

2. Now you are exalted to the highest place,
   King of the heavens, where one day I'll bow.
   But for now I marvel at this saving grace,
   and I'm full of praise once again,
   I'm full of praise once again.

121 Jesus Christ is risen today

v.1 'Surrexit hodie (14th century)
trans. anon. as in 'Lyra Davidica' (1708);
vs. 2-3 from J. Arnold's 'Compleat Psalmodist' (1749)

Melody from 'Lyra Davidica' (1708)
harm. William Henry Monk (1823-1889)

EASTER HYMN 77 77 and Alleluias

1. Je - sus Christ is ris'n to - day, al - le - lu - ia!
our tri - um - phant ho - ly day, al - le - lu - ia!
who did once, u - pon the cross, al - le - lu - ia!
suf - fer to re - deem our loss, al - le - lu - ia!

2. Hymns of praise then let us sing, alleluia!
unto Christ, our heav'nly King, alleluia!
who endured the cross and grave, alleluia!
sinners to redeem and save, alleluia!

3. But the pains that he endured, alleluia!
our salvation have procured; alleluia!
now above the sky he's King, alleluia!
where the angels ever sing, alleluia!

122 Jesus, good above all other

Percy Dearmer (1867-1936)
after John Mason Neale (1818-1866) alt.

German Carol melody (14th century)
harm. Ralph Vaughan Williams (1872-1958)

QUEM PASTORES 88 87

1. Je - sus, good a - bove all o - ther, gen - tle child of
gen - tle mo - ther, in a sta - ble born our
bro - ther, give us grace to per - se - vere.

2. Jesus, cradled in a manger,
for us facing ev'ry danger,
living as a homeless stranger,
make we thee our King most dear.

3. Jesus, for thy people dying,
risen Master, death defying,
Lord in heav'n thy grace supplying,
keep us to thy presence near.

4. Jesus, who our sorrows bearest,
all our thoughts and hopes thou sharest,
thou to us the truth declarest;
help us all thy truth to hear.

5. Lord, in all our doings guide us;
pride and hate shall ne'er divide us;
we'll go on with thee beside us,
and with joy we'll persevere.

123 Jesus is Lord! Creation's voice proclaims it

David J. Mansell

David J. Mansell

JESUS IS LORD 11 12 11 12 and Refrain

Unison

1. Je - sus is Lord! Cre - a - tion's voice pro - claims it,

for by his pow'r each tree and flow'r was planned and made.

Je - sus is Lord! The u - ni - verse de - clares it;

sun, moon and stars in hea - ven cry: Je - sus is Lord!

Refrain

Je - sus is Lord! Je - sus is Lord!

Praise him with al - le - lu - ias, for Je - sus is Lord!

2. Jesus is Lord! Yet from his throne eternal
   in flesh he came to die in pain on Calv'ry's tree.
   Jesus is Lord! From him all life proceeding,
   yet gave his life as ransom thus setting us free.

3. Jesus is Lord! O'er sin the mighty conqu'ror,
   from death he rose and all his foes shall own his name.
   Jesus is Lord! God sends his Holy Spirit
   to show by works of power that Jesus is Lord.

124 Jesus lives! thy terrors now

Christian Fürchtegott Gellert (1715-1769)
trans. Frances Elizabeth Cox (1812-1897) alt.

Henry John Gauntlett (1805-1876)

ST ALBINUS 78 78 and Alleluia

1. Je - sus lives! thy ter - rors now can no more, O
death, ap - pal us; Je - sus lives! by this we know
thou, O grave, canst not en - thral us. Al - le - lu - ia.

2. Jesus lives! henceforth is death
   but the gate of life immortal:
   this shall calm our trembling breath,
   when we pass its gloomy portal.
   Alleluia.

3. Jesus lives! for us he died;
   then, alone to Jesus living,
   pure in heart may we abide,
   glory to our Saviour giving.
   Alleluia.

4. Jesus lives! our hearts know well
   naught from us his love shall sever;
   life nor death nor pow'rs of hell
   tear us from his keeping ever.
   Alleluia.

5. Jesus lives! to him the throne
   over all the world is given:
   may we go where he is gone,
   rest and reign with him in heaven.
   Alleluia.

125 Jesus shall reign

Isaac Watts (1674-1748) alt.

Melody from Thomas Williams'
'Psalmodia Evangelica' (1789)

TRURO LM

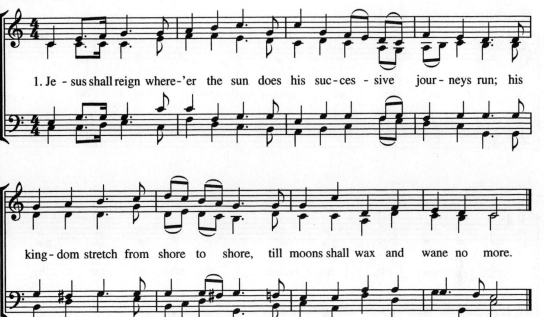

1. Je - sus shall reign where-'er the sun does his suc - ces - sive jour - neys run; his

king - dom stretch from shore to shore, till moons shall wax and wane no more.

2. People and realms of ev'ry tongue
   dwell on his love with sweetest song,
   and infant voices shall proclaim
   their early blessings on his name.

3. Blessings abound where'er he reigns:
   the pris'ners leap to lose their chains;
   the weary find eternal rest,
   and all the humble poor are blest.

4. To him shall endless prayer be made
   and praises throng to crown his head;
   his name like incense shall arise
   with ev'ry morning sacrifice.

5. Let ev'ry creature rise and bring
   peculiar honours to our King;
   angels descend with songs again,
   and earth repeat the loud amen.

126 Jesu, the very thought of thee

St Bernard of Clairvaux (1091-1153)
trans. Edward Caswall (1814-1878) alt.

John Bacchus Dykes (1823-1876)

ST AGNES (DYKES) CM

1. Je - su, the ve - ry thought of thee

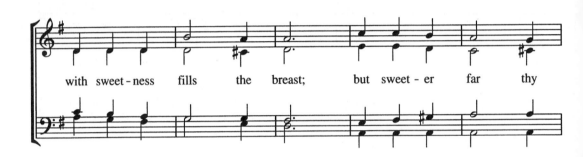

with sweet-ness fills the breast; but sweet - er far thy

face to see, and in thy pre - sence rest.

2. No voice can sing, no heart can frame,
   nor can the mem'ry find,
   a sweeter sound than Jesu's name,
   the Saviour of mankind.

3. O hope of ev'ry contrite heart,
   O joy of all the meek,
   to those who ask how kind thou art,
   how good to those who seek!

4. But what to those who find? Ah, this
   nor tongue nor pen can show;
   the love of Jesus, what it is
   his true disciples know.

5. Jesu, our only joy be thou,
   as thou our prize wilt be;
   in thee be all our glory now,
   and through eternity.

127 Jubilate, everybody

Fred Dunn

Fred Dunn (1907-1979)

JUBILATE DEO 88 87 88 86

Ju - bi-la - te, ev - 'ry-bo - dy, serve the Lord in all your ways and

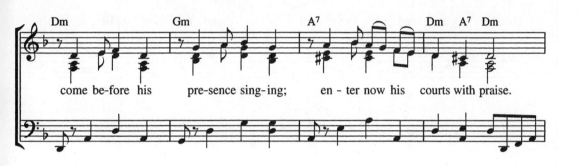

come be-fore his pre-sence sing-ing; en - ter now his courts with praise.

For the Lord our God is gra - cious, and his mer - cy e - ver-last - ing.

Ju - bi-la - te, ju - bi-la - te, ju - bi-la - te De - o!

128 Just as I am, without one plea

Charlotte Elliott (1789-1871)   Henry Smart (1813-1879)

MISERICORDIA 88 86

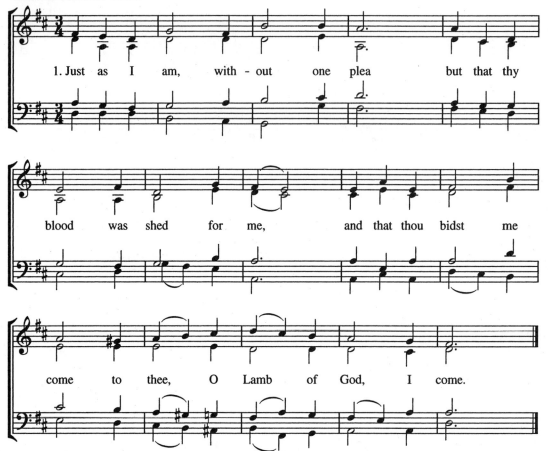

1. Just as I am, with-out one plea but that thy
blood was shed for me, and that thou bidst me
come to thee, O Lamb of God, I come.

2. Just as I am, though tossed about
with many a conflict, many a doubt,
fightings and fears within, without,
O Lamb of God, I come.

3. Just as I am, poor, wretched, blind;
sight, riches, healing of the mind,
yea, all I need, in thee to find,
O Lamb of God, I come.

4. Just as I am, thou wilt receive,
wilt welcome, pardon, cleanse, relieve:
because thy promise I believe,
O Lamb of God, I come.

5. Just as I am, thy love unknown
has broken ev'ry barrier down,
now to be thine, yea, thine alone,
O Lamb of God, I come.

6. Just as I am, of that free love
the breadth, length, depth and height to prove,
here for a season, then above,
O Lamb of God, I come.

129 King of glory, King of peace

George Herbert (1593-1633)

John David Jones (1827-1870)

GWALCHMAI 74 74 D

1. King of glo - ry, King of peace, I will love thee;

and, that love may ne - ver cease, I will move thee.

Thou hast gran - ted my ap - peal, thou hast heard me;

thou didst note my ar - dent zeal, thou hast spared me.

2. Wherefore with my utmost art,
   I will sing thee,
   and the cream of all my heart
   I will bring thee.
   Though my sins against me cried,
   thou didst clear me,
   and alone, when they replied,
   thou didst hear me.

3. Sev'n whole days, not one in sev'n,
   I will praise thee;
   in my heart, though not in heav'n,
   I can raise thee.
   Small it is, in this poor sort
   to enrol thee:
   e'en eternity's too short
   to extol thee.

130 Lead, kindly light

John Henry Newman (1801-1890)

Charles Henry Purday (1799-1885)

TUNE 1: SANDON 10 4 10 4 10 10

1. Lead, kind-ly light, a - mid th'en-cir-cling gloom, lead thou me on; the night is dark, and I am far from home; lead thou me on. Keep thou my feet; I do not ask to see the dis - tant scene; one step e - nough for me.

2. I was not ever thus, nor prayed that thou
   shouldst lead me on;
   I loved to choose and see my path; but now
   lead thou me on.
   I loved the garish day, and, spite of fears,
   pride ruled my will: remember not past years.

3. So long thy pow'r hath blest me, sure it still
   will lead me on,
   o'er moor and fen, o'er crag and torrent, till
   the night is gone;
   and with the morn those angel faces smile,
   which I have loved long since, and lost awhile.

John Henry Newman (1801-1890)

John Bacchus Dykes (1823-1876)

TUNE 2: LUX BENIGNA 10 4 10 4 10 10

131 Lead us, heavenly Father, lead us

James Edmeston (1791-1867)

Friedrich Filitz (1804-1876)

MANNHEIM 87 87 87

1. Lead us, heav'n-ly Fa - ther, lead us o'er the world's tem - pes - tuous sea;

guard us, guide us, keep us, feed us, for we have no help but thee;

yet pos - ses - sing ev - 'ry bles - sing if our God our Fa - ther be.

2. Saviour, breathe forgiveness o'er us,
   all our weakness thou dost know,
   thou didst tread this earth before us,
   thou didst feel its keenest woe;
   lone and dreary, faint and weary,
   through the desert thou didst go.

3. Spirit of our God, descending,
   fill our hearts with heav'nly joy,
   love with ev'ry passion blending,
   pleasure that can never cloy;
   thus provided, pardoned, guided,
   nothing can our peace destroy.

132 Let all the world in every corner sing

George Herbert (1593-1633)

Basil Harwood (1859-1949)

LUCKINGTON 10 4 66 66 10 4

1. Let all the world in ev-'ry cor-ner sing, my God and King! The heav'ns are not too high, his praise may thi-ther fly; the earth is not too low, his prai-ses there may grow. Let all the world in ev-'ry cor-ner sing, my God and King!

2. Let all the world in ev'ry corner sing,
   my God and King!
   The Church with psalms must shout,
   no door can keep them out;
   but, above all, the heart
   must bear the longest part.
   Let all the world in ev'ry corner sing,
   my God and King!

133 Let us, with a gladsome mind

John Milton (1608-1674)
based on Psalm 136
MONKLAND 77 77

From 'Hymn Tunes of the United Brethren'
adapt. by John Bernard Wilkes (1785-1869)

1. Let us, with a glad - some mind, praise the Lord, for he is kind;

Refrain

for his mer - cies ay en - dure, e - ver faith - ful, e - ver sure.

2. Let us blaze his name abroad,
   for of gods he is the God;

3. He, with all-commanding might,
   filled the new-made world with light;

4. He the golden-tressèd sun
   caused all day his course to run;

5. And the moon to shine at night,
   'mid her starry sisters bright;

6. All things living he doth feed,
   his full hand supplies their need;

7. Let us, with a gladsome mind,
   praise the Lord, for he is kind;

134 Lift high the Cross

George William Kitchin (1827-1912)
Michael Robert Newbolt (1874-1956) alt.

Sydney Hugo Nicholson (1875-1947)

CRUCIFER 10 10 and Refrain

2. Led on their way by this triumphant sign,
   the hosts of God in joyful praise combine:

3. Each new disciple of the Crucified
   is called to bear the seal of him who died:

4. Saved by the Cross whereon their Lord was slain,
   now Adam's children their lost home regain:

5. From north and south, from east and west they raise
   in growing harmony their song of praise:

6. O Lord, once lifted on the glorious tree,
   as thou hast promised, draw us unto thee:

7. Let ev'ry race and ev'ry language tell
   of him who saves from fear of death and hell:

8. From farthest regions, let them homage bring,
   and on his Cross adore their Saviour King:

9. Set up thy throne, that earth's despair may cease
   beneath the shadow of its healing peace:

10. For thy blest Cross which doth for all atone,
    creation's praises rise before thy throne:

11. So let the world proclaim with one accord
    the praises of our ever-living Lord.

135 Light's abode, celestial Salem

Ascribed to Thomas à Kempis (c.1379-1471)
trans. John Mason Neale (1818-1866)

Henry Smart (1813-1879)

REGENT SQUARE 87 87 87

1. Light's a-bode, ce - les - tial Sa -lem, vi - sion whence true peace doth spring,
bright- er than the heart can fan - cy, man-sion of the high - est King;
O how glo -rious are the prai - ses which of thee the pro-phets sing!

2. There for ever and for ever
alleluia is outpoured;
for unending, for unbroken
is the feast-day of the Lord;
all is pure and all is holy
that within thy walls is stored.

3. There no cloud or passing vapour
dims the brightness of the air;
endless noon-day, glorious noon-day,
from the Sun of suns is there;
there no night brings rest from labour,
for unknown are toil and care.

4. O how glorious and resplendent,
fragile body, shalt thou be,
when endued with so much beauty,
full of health and strong and free,
full of vigour, full of pleasure
that shall last eternally.

5. Now with gladness, now with courage,
bear the burden on thee laid,
that hereafter these thy labour
may with endless gifts be paid;
and in everlasting glory
thou with brightness be arrayed.

6. Laud and honour to the Father,
laud and honour to the Son,
laud and honour to the Spirit,
ever Three and ever One,
consubstantial, co-eternal,
while unending ages run.

136 Lo, he comes with clouds descending

Charles Wesley (1707-1788),
John Cennick (1718-1755)
and Martin Madan (1726-1790) alt.

From John Wesley's
'Select Hymns with Tunes Annext' (1765)

HELMSLEY 87 87 47

1. Lo, he comes with clouds des - cend - ing,

once for mor - tal sin - ners slain; thou - sand

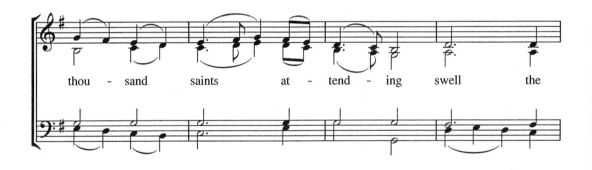

thou - sand saints at - tend - ing swell the

tri - umph of his train. Al - le -

lu - ia! Al - le - lu - ia! Al - le -

lu - ia! Christ ap - pears on earth to reign.

2. Ev'ry eye shall now behold him
robed in dreadful majesty;
we who set at naught and sold him,
pierced and nailed him to the tree,
deeply grieving, deeply grieving, deeply grieving,
shall the true Messiah see.

3. Those dear tokens of his passion
still his dazzling body bears,
cause of endless exultation
to his ransomed worshippers:
with what rapture, with what rapture, with what rapture
gaze we on those glorious scars!

4. Yea, amen, let all adore thee,
high on thine eternal throne;
Saviour, take the pow'r and glory,
claim the kingdom for thine own.
Alleluia! Alleluia! Alleluia!
Thou shalt reign, and thou alone.

137 Lord, for the years

Timothy Dudley-Smith (b.1926)

Michael Baughen (b.1930)
arr. David Iliff

LORD OF THE YEARS 11 10 11 10

1. Lord, for the years your love has kept and gui-ded, urged and in-spired us, cheered us on our way, sought us and saved us, par-doned and pro-vi-ded, Lord of the years, we bring our thanks to-day.

2. Lord, for that word, the word of life
   which fires us,
   speaks to our hearts and sets our souls ablaze,
   teaches and trains, rebukes us and inspires us,
   Lord of the word, receive your people's praise.

3. Lord, for our land, in this our generation,
   spirits oppressed by pleasure, wealth and care;
   for young and old, for commonwealth and nation,
   Lord of our land, be pleased to hear our prayer.

4. Lord, for our world; when we disown
   and doubt him,
   loveless in strength, and comfortless in pain;
   hungry and helpless, lost indeed without him,
   Lord of the world, we pray that Christ may reign.

5. Lord, for ourselves; in living power remake us,
   self on the cross and Christ upon the throne;
   past put behind us, for the future take us,
   Lord of our lives, to live for Christ alone.

138 Lord Jesus Christ

Living Lord

Patrick Appleford

Patrick Appleford (b.1925)

LIVING LORD 9 8 88 83

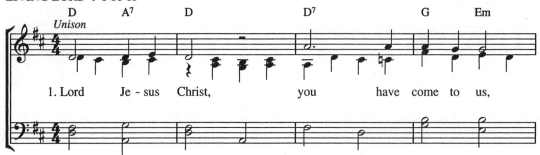

1. Lord Je - sus Christ, you have come to us,

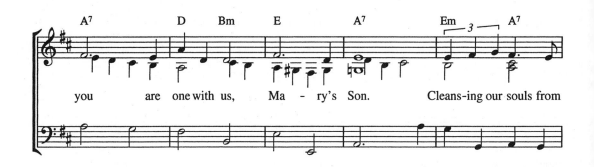

you are one with us, Ma - ry's Son. Cleans-ing our souls from

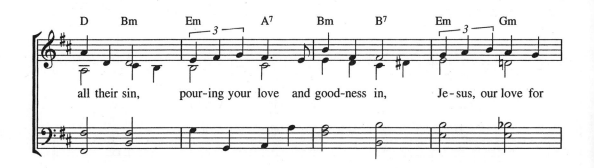

all their sin, pour-ing your love and good-ness in, Je - sus, our love for

To next verse

Last time

you we sing, liv - ing Lord. Lord.

2. Lord Jesus Christ,
   now and ev'ry day
   teach us how to pray,
   Son of God.
   You have commanded us to do
   this in remembrance, Lord, of you.
   Into our lives your pow'r breaks through,
   living Lord.

3. Lord Jesus Christ,
   you have come to us,
   born as one of us,
   Mary's Son.
   Led out to die on Calvary,
   risen from death to set us free,
   living Lord Jesus, help us see
   you are Lord.

4. Lord Jesus Christ,
   I would come to you,
   live my life for you,
   Son of God.
   All your commands I know are true,
   your many gifts will make me new,
   into my life your pow'r breaks through,
   living Lord.

139 Lord Jesus, think on me

'Mnōeo Christe' by
Bishop Synesius (375-430)
trans. Allen William Chatfield (1808-1896)

From 'The Psalmes in English Metre' (1579)
adapted by William Damon (1540-1591)

SOUTHWELL (DAMON) SM

1. Lord Je-sus, think on me, and purge a-way my sin; from

earth-born pas-sions set me free, and make me pure with-in.

2. Lord Jesus, think on me,
   with care and woe opprest;
   let me thy loving servant be,
   and taste thy promised rest.

3. Lord Jesus, think on me
   amid the battle's strife;
   in all my pain and misery
   be thou my health and life.

4. Lord Jesus, think on me,
   nor let me go astray;
   through darkness and perplexity
   point thou the heav'nly way.

5. Lord Jesus, think on me,
   when flows the tempest high:
   when on doth rush the enemy,
   O Saviour, be thou nigh.

6. Lord Jesus, think on me,
   that, when the flood is past,
   I may th'eternal brightness see,
   and share thy joy at last.

140 Lord of all hopefulness

Jan Struther (1901-1953)

Traditional Irish melody
arr. Colin Hand

SLANE 10 11 11 12

1. Lord of all hope-ful-ness, Lord of all joy, whose trust, e-ver child-like, no cares could des-troy, be there at our wak-ing, and give us, we pray, your bliss in our hearts, Lord, at the break of the day.

2. Lord of all eagerness,
Lord of all faith,
whose strong hands were skilled
at the plane and the lathe,
be there at our labours,
and give us, we pray,
your strength in our hearts, Lord,
at the noon of the day.

3. Lord of all kindliness,
Lord of all grace,
your hands swift to welcome,
your arms to embrace,
be there at our homing,
and give us, we pray,
your love in our hearts, Lord,
at the eve of the day.

4. Lord of all gentleness,
Lord of all calm,
whose voice is contentment,
whose presence is balm,
be there at our sleeping,
and give us, we pray,
your peace in our hearts, Lord,
at the end of the day.

141 Lord, the light of your love

Shine, Jesus, shine

Graham Kendrick

Graham Kendrick (b.1950)

SHINE, JESUS, SHINE 9 9 10 10 6

1. Lord, the light of your love is shin - ing, in the midst of the dark - ness, shin - ing; Je - sus, Light of the World, shine up - on us, set us free by the truth you now bring us. Shine on me, shine on me.

Refrain

Shine, Je-sus, shine, fill this land with the Fa-ther's glo-ry;
Flow, ri-ver, flow, flood the na-tions with grace and mer-cy;

blaze, Spi-rit, blaze, set our hearts on fire.
send forth your word, Lord, and

let there be light.

2. Lord, I come to your awesome presence,
   from the shadows into your radiance;
   by the blood I may enter your brightness,
   search me, try me, consume all my darkness.
   Shine on me, shine on me.

3. As we gaze on your kingly brightness,
   so our faces display your likeness,
   ever changing from glory to glory;
   mirrored here may our lives tell your story.
   Shine on me, shine on me.

   (Refrain twice to end)

142 Lord, thy word abideth

Henry Williams Baker (1821-1877)

Melody from M. Weisse's
'Neu Gesangbüchlein' (1531) adapted by
William Henry Monk (1823-1889)

RAVENSHAW 66 66

1. Lord, thy word a - bi - deth, and our foot- steps guid - eth;

who its truth be - liev - eth light and joy re - ceiv - eth.

2. When our foes are near us,
   then thy word doth cheer us,
   word of consolation,
   message of salvation.

3. When the storms are o'er us,
   and dark clouds before us,
   then its light directeth,
   and our way protecteth.

4. Who can tell the pleasure,
   who recount the treasure,
   by thy word imparted
   to the simple-hearted?

5. Word of mercy, giving
   succour to the living;
   word of life, supplying
   comfort to the dying.

6. O that we, discerning
   its most holy learning,
   Lord, may love and fear thee,
   evermore be near thee.

143 Love divine, all loves excelling

Charles Wesley (1707-1788) alt.

John Stainer (1840-1901)

TUNE 1: LOVE DIVINE 87 87

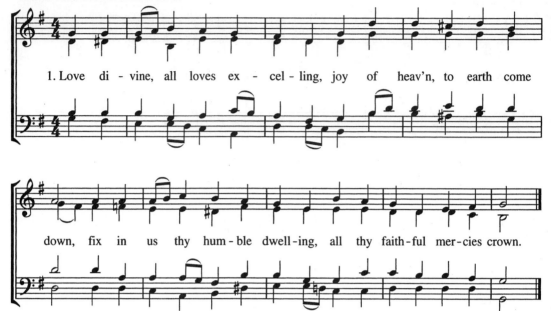

1. Love di - vine, all loves ex - cel - ling, joy of heav'n, to earth come down, fix in us thy hum - ble dwell - ing, all thy faith - ful mer - cies crown.

2. Jesu, thou art all compassion,
   pure unbounded love thou art;
   visit us with thy salvation,
   enter ev'ry trembling heart.

3. Breathe, O breathe thy loving Spirit
   into ev'ry troubled breast;
   let us all in thee inherit,
   let us find thy promised rest.

4. Take away the love of sinning,
   Alpha and Omega be;
   end of faith, as its beginning,
   set our hearts at liberty.

5. Come, almighty to deliver,
   let us all thy grace receive;
   suddenly return, and never,
   nevermore thy temples leave.

6. Thee we would be always blessing,
   serve thee as thy hosts above;
   pray, and praise thee without ceasing,
   glory in thy perfect love.

7. Finish then thy new creation,
   pure and spotless let us be;
   let us see thy great salvation
   perfectly restored in thee.

8. Changed from glory into glory,
   till in heav'n we take our place,
   till we cast our crowns before thee,
   lost in wonder, love, and praise.

Charles Wesley (1707-1788) alt.

William Penfro Rowlands (1860-1937)

TUNE 2: BLAENWERN 87 87 D

1. Love di - vine, all loves ex - cel - ling, joy of heav'n, to earth come down, fix in us thy hum - ble dwell - ing, all thy faith - ful mer - cies crown. Je - su, thou art all com - pas - sion, pure un - bound - ed love thou art; vi - sit us with thy sal - va - tion, en - ter ev - 'ry trem - bling heart.

144 Love's redeeming work is done

Charles Wesley (1707-1788)

John Wesley's 'Foundery Collection' (1742)

SAVANNAH 77 77

1. Love's re - deem-ing work is done; fought the fight, the bat - tle won: lo, our Sun's e - clipse is o'er, lo, he sets in blood no more.

2. Vain the stone, the watch, the seal;
   Christ has burst the gates of hell;
   death in vain forbids his rise;
   Christ has opened paradise.

3. Lives again our glorious King;
   where, O death, is now thy sting?
   Dying once, he all doth save;
   where thy victory, O grave?

4. Soar we now where Christ has led,
   foll'wing our exalted Head;
   made like him, like him we rise;
   ours the cross, the grave, the skies.

5. Hail the Lord of earth and heav'n!
   praise to thee by both be giv'n;
   thee we greet triumphant now;
   hail, the Resurrection thou!

145 Loving Shepherd of thy sheep

Jane Elizabeth Leeson (1809-1881)   Leighton George Hayne (1836-1883)

BUCKLAND 77 77

1. Lov-ing Shep-herd of thy sheep, keep me, Lord, in safe-ty keep; no-thing can thy pow'r with-stand, none can pluck me from thy hand.

2. Loving Shepherd, thou didst give
thine own life that I might live;
may I love thee day by day,
gladly thy sweet will obey.

3. Loving Shepherd, ever near,
teach me still thy voice to hear;
suffer not my steps to stray
from the straight and narrow way.

4. Where thou leadest may I go,
walking in thy steps below;
then, before thy Father's throne,
Jesu, claim me for thine own.

146 Majesty, worship his majesty

Jack W. Hayford

Jack W. Hayford (b.1934)

Ma - jes-ty, wor-ship his ma - jes-ty; un - to

Je - sus be glo - ry, hon-our and praise.

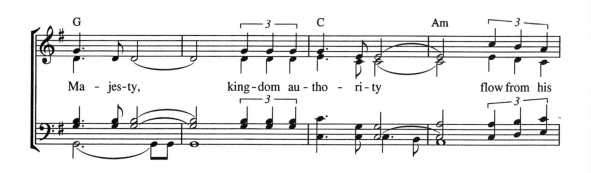

Ma - jes-ty, king-dom au - tho - ri-ty flow from his

throne un - to his own: his an-them raise. So ex -

alt, lift up on high the name of Je - sus; mag - ni -

fy, come glo - ri - fy Christ Je - sus the King.

Ma - jes-ty, wor-ship his ma - jes-ty, Je - sus who

died, now glo - ri - fied, King of all kings.

147 Make me a channel of your peace

Sebastian Temple
based on the Prayer of St Francis

Sebastian Temple (1928-1997)

2. Make me a channel of your peace.
   Where there's despair in life, let me bring hope.
   Where there is darkness, only light,
   and where there's sadness, ever joy.

3. Make me a channel of your peace.
   It is in pardoning that we are pardoned,
   in giving of ourselves that we receive,
   and in dying that we're born to eternal life.

148 Make way, make way

Graham Kendrick

Graham Kendrick (b.1950)

1. Make way, make way, for Christ the King in splen - dour ar - rives; fling wide the gates and wel - come him in - to your lives. Make way, *make way*, make way, *make way*, for the King of kings; *for the King of kings*; make way, *make way*, make way, *make way*, and let his king - dom in!

2. He comes the broken hearts to heal,
the pris'ners to free;
the deaf shall hear, the lame shall dance,
the blind shall see.

3. And those who mourn with heavy hearts,
who weep and sigh,
with laughter, joy and royal crown
he'll beautify.

4. We call you now to worship him
as Lord of all,
to have no gods before him,
their thrones must fall.

149 Meekness and majesty

This is your God

Graham Kendrick

Graham Kendrick (b.1950)

THIS IS YOUR GOD 66 65 D and Refrain

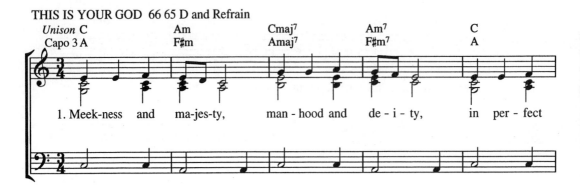

1. Meek-ness and ma-jes-ty, man-hood and de-i-ty, in per-fect

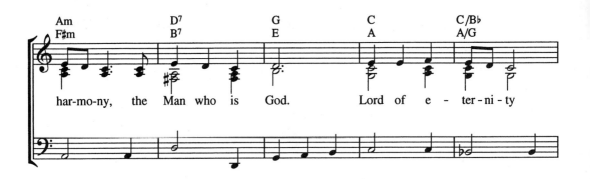

har-mo-ny, the Man who is God. Lord of e-ter-ni-ty

dwells in hu-ma-ni-ty, kneels in hu-mi-li-ty and wash-es our

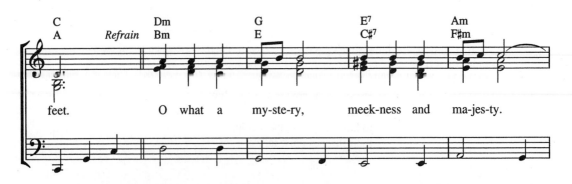

feet. O what a my-ste-ry, meek-ness and ma-jes-ty.

2. Father's pure radiance,
   perfect in innocence,
   yet learns obedience
   to death on a cross.
   Suff'ring to give us life,
   conqu'ring through sacrifice,
   and as they crucify
   prays: 'Father forgive.'

3. Wisdom unsearchable,
   God the invisible,
   love indestructible
   in frailty appears.
   Lord of infinity,
   stooping so tenderly,
   lifts our humanity
   to the heights of his throne.

150 Morning has broken

Eleanor Farjeon (1881-1965)

Traditional Gaelic melody
arr. Colin Hand

BUNESSAN 55 54 D

Unison

1. Morn-ing has bro-ken like the first morn-ing, black-bird has spo-ken like the first bird. Praise for the sing-ing! Praise for the morn-ing! Praise for them, spring-ing fresh from the Word!

2. Sweet the rain's new fall,
   sunlit from heaven,
   like the first dew-fall
   on the first grass.
   Praise for the sweetness
   of the wet garden,
   sprung in completeness
   where his feet pass.

3. Mine is the sunlight!
   Mine is the morning
   born of the one light
   Eden saw play!
   Praise with elation,
   praise ev'ry morning,
   God's re-creation
   of the new day!

151 My God, and is thy table spread

Philip Doddridge (1702-1751) alt.
v.3: Michael Forster (b.1946)

From A. Williams' 'Second supplement
to Psalmody in Miniature' (c.1780)
adapted by Edward Miller (1735-1807)

ROCKINGHAM LM

1. My God, and is thy table spread, and does thy cup with love o'er-flow? Thi-ther be all thy chil-dren led, and let them all thy sweet-ness know.

2. Hail, sacred feast, which Jesus makes!
   Rich banquet of his flesh and blood!
   Thrice happy all, who here partake
   that sacred stream, that heav'nly food.

3. What wondrous love! What perfect grace,
   for Jesus, our exalted host,
   invites us to this special place
   who offer least and need the most.

4. O let thy table honoured be,
   and furnished well with joyful guests:
   and may each soul salvation see,
   that here its sacred pledges tastes.

152 My God, I love thee

Latin (17th century)
trans. Edward Caswall (1814-1878)

John Stainer (1840-1901)

ST FRANCIS XAVIER CM

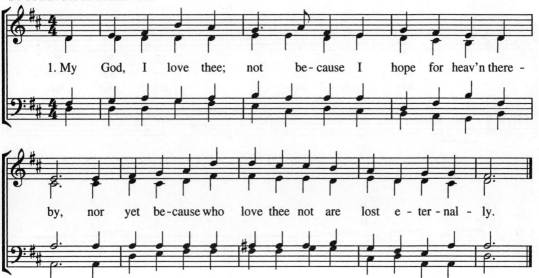

1. My God, I love thee; not be-cause I hope for heav'n there -
by, nor yet be-cause who love thee not are lost e - ter - nal - ly.

2. Thou, O my Jesus, thou didst me
   upon the cross embrace;
   for me didst bear the nails and spear,
   and manifold disgrace.

3. And griefs and torments numberless,
   and sweat of agony;
   yea, death itself – and all for me
   who was thine enemy.

4. Then why, O blessèd Jesu Christ,
   should I not love thee well?
   Not for the sake of winning heav'n,
   nor of escaping hell.

5. Not from the hope of gaining aught,
   not seeking a reward;
   but as thyself hast lovèd me,
   O ever-loving Lord.

6. So would I love thee, dearest Lord,
   and in thy praise will sing;
   solely because thou art my God,
   and my most loving King.

153 My Jesus, my Saviour

Shout to the Lord

Darlene Zschech

Darlene Zschech

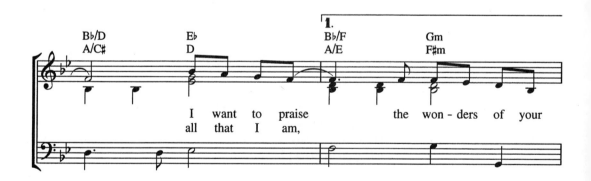

154 My song is love unknown

Samuel Crossman (c.1624-1684) alt.

John Ireland (1879-1962)

LOVE UNKNOWN 66 66 44 44

1. My song is love un-known, my Sa-viour's love to me, love to the love-less shown, that they might love-ly be. O who am I, that for my sake, my Lord should take frail flesh and die?

2. He came from his blest throne,
salvation to bestow;
but men refused, and none
the longed-for Christ would know.
But O, my friend, my friend indeed,
who at my need his life did spend!

3. Sometimes they strew his way,
and his sweet praises sing;
resounding all the day
hosannas to their King;
then 'Crucify!' is all their breath,
and for his death they thirst and cry.

4. Why, what hath my Lord done?
What makes this rage and spite?
He made the lame to run,
he gave the blind their sight.
Sweet injuries! Yet they at these
themselves displease, and 'gainst him rise.

5. They rise, and needs will have
my dear Lord made away;
a murderer they save,
the Prince of Life they slay.
Yet cheerful he to suff'ring goes,
that he his foes from thence might free.

6 Here might I stay and sing,
no story so divine;
never was love, dear King,
never was grief like thine.
This is my friend in whose sweet praise
I all my days could gladly spend.

155 Nearer my God, to thee

Sarah Flower Adams (1805-1848)   Lowell Mason (1792-1872)

BETHANY 64 64 66 64

1. Near - er, my God, to thee, near - er to thee! E'en though it be a cross that rais - eth me: still all my song would be, 'Near - er, my God, to thee, near - er, my God to thee, near - er to thee.'

2. Though, like the wanderer,
   the sun gone down,
   darkness be over me,
   my rest like a stone;
   yet in my dreams I'd be
   nearer, my God, to thee, *(x2)*
   nearer to thee!

3. There let the way appear,
   steps unto heav'n;
   all that thou sendest me
   in mercy giv'n:
   angels to beckon me
   nearer, my God, to thee, *(x2)*
   nearer to thee!

4. Then, with my waking thoughts
   bright with thy praise,
   out of my stony griefs
   Bethel I'll raise;
   so by my woes to be
   nearer, my God, to thee, *(x2)*
   nearer to thee!

5. Or if on joyful wing
   cleaving the sky,
   sun, moon and stars forgot,
   upwards I fly,
   still all my song shall be,
   'Nearer, my God, to thee, *(x2)*
   nearer to thee.'

156 New every morning is the love

John Keble (1792-1866)
based on Lamentations 3:23

Samuel Webbe (1740-1816)

MELCOMBE LM

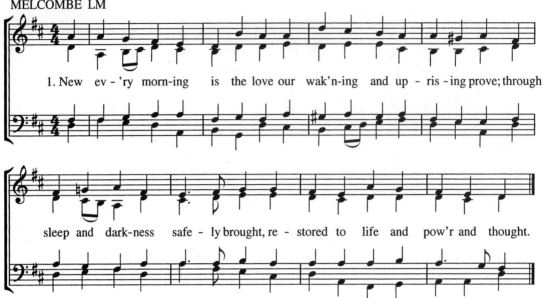

1. New ev-'ry morn-ing is the love our wak'n-ing and up - ris -ing prove; through

sleep and dark-ness safe - ly brought, re - stored to life and pow'r and thought.

2. New mercies, each returning day,
   hover around us while we pray;
   new perils past, new sins forgiv'n,
   new thoughts of God, new hopes of heav'n.

3. If on our daily course our mind
   be set to hallow all we find,
   new treasures still, of countless price,
   God will provide for sacrifice.

4. Old friends, old scenes, will lovelier be,
   as more of heav'n in each we see;
   some soft'ning gleam of love and prayer
   shall dawn on ev'ry cross and care.

5. The trivial round, the common task,
   will furnish all we need to ask,
   room to deny ourselves, a road
   to bring us daily nearer God.

6. Only, O Lord, in thy dear love
   fit us for perfect rest above;
   and help us, this and ev'ry day,
   to live more nearly as we pray.

157 Now thank we all our God

'Nun danket alle Gott'
by Martin Rinkart (1586-1649)
trans. Catherine Winkworth (1827-1878)

Melody by Johann Crüger (1598-1662)
harm. William Henry Monk (1823-1889)

NUN DANKET 67 67 66 66

1. Now thank we all our God, with hearts and hands and voi - ces, who won - drous things hath done, in whom his world re - joic - es; who from our mo - ther's arms hath blessed us on our way with count - less gifts of love, and still is ours to - day.

2. O may this bounteous God
through all our life be near us,
with ever joyful hearts
and blessèd peace to cheer us;
and keep us in his grace,
and guide us when perplexed,
and free us from all ills
in this world and the next.

3. All praise and thanks to God
the Father now be given,
the Son and him who reigns
with them in highest heaven,
the one eternal God,
whom earth and heav'n adore;
for thus it was, is now,
and shall be evermore.

158 Now the green blade riseth

John Macleod Campbell Crum (1872-1958) alt.

NOEL NOUVELET 11 11 10 11

Traditional French melody
arr. Christopher Tambling

1. Now the green blade ris - eth from the bur - ied grain,
wheat that in the dark earth ma - ny days has lain;
Love lives a - gain, that with the dead has been;
Love is come a - gain, like wheat that spring - eth green.

2. In the grave they laid him, Love by hatred slain,
   thinking that never he would wake again,
   laid in the earth like grain that sleeps unseen:
   Love is come again, like wheat that springeth green.

3. Forth he came at Easter, like the risen grain,
   he that for three days in the grave had lain;
   quick from the dead, my risen Lord is seen:
   Love is come again, like wheat that springeth green.

4. When our hearts are wintry, grieving or in pain,
   thy touch can call us back to life again;
   fields of our hearts, that dead and bare have been:
   Love is come again, like wheat that springeth green.

159 O Breath of Life

Elizabeth Ann Porter Head (1850-1936)　　　　　　Mary Jane Hammond (1878-1964)

SPIRITUS VITAE 98 98

1. O Breath of Life, come sweep-ing through us, re - vive your Church with life and pow'r; O Breath of Life, come cleanse, re - new us, and fit your Church to meet this hour.

2. O Breath of Love, come breathe within us,
   renewing thought and will and heart;
   come, love of Christ, afresh to win us,
   revive your Church in ev'ry part!

3. O Wind of God, come bend us, break us,
   till humbly we confess our need;
   then in your tenderness remake us,
   revive, restore – for this we plead.

4. Revive us, Lord; is zeal abating
   while harvest fields are vast and white?
   Revive us, Lord, the world is waiting –
   equip thy Church to spread the light.

160 O come, all ye faithful

Original Latin attributed to John Francis Wade
trans. Frederick Oakeley (1802-1880)

Attributed to John Francis Wade (1711-1786)

ADESTE FIDELES Irregular and Refrain

1. O come, all ye faith - ful, joy - ful and tri - um - phant, O
come ye, O come ye to Beth - le - hem;
come and be - hold him, born the king of an - gels:

Refrain

O come,
O come, let us a - dore him, O come, let us a - dore him, O
come, let us a - dore him, Christ the Lord.

2. God of God,
   Light of Light,
   lo, he abhors not the Virgin's womb;
   very God, begotten not created:

3. See how the shepherds,
   summoned to his cradle,
   leaving their flocks, draw nigh with lowly fear;
   we too will thither bend our joyful footsteps:

4. Lo, star-led chieftains,
   Magi, Christ adoring,
   offer him incense, gold and myrrh;
   we to the Christ-child bring our hearts' oblations:

5. Child, for us sinners
   poor and in the manger,
   fain we embrace thee, with love and awe;
   who would not love thee, loving us so dearly?

6. Sing, choirs of angels,
   sing in exultation,
   sing, all ye citizens of heav'n above;
   glory to God in the highest:

7. Yea, Lord, we greet thee,
   born this happy morning,
   Jesu, to thee be glory giv'n;
   Word of the Father, now in flesh appearing:

161 O come, O come, Emmanuel

From the 'Great O Antiphons' (12th-13th century)
trans. John Mason Neale (1818-1866)

Adapted by Thomas Helmore (1811-1890)
from a French Missal
arr. Colin Hand

VENI EMMANUEL LM and Refrain

1. O come, O come, Emmanuel, and ransom captive Israel, that mourns in lonely exile here, until the Son of God appear. Rejoice, rejoice! Emmanuel shall come to thee, O Israel.

2. O come, thou rod of Jesse, free
   thine own from Satan's tyranny;
   from depths of hell thy people save,
   and give them vict'ry o'er the grave.

3. O come, thou dayspring, come and cheer
   our spirits by thine advent here;
   disperse the gloomy clouds of night,
   and death's dark shadows put to flight.

4. O come, thou key of David, come
   and open wide our heav'nly home;
   make safe the way that leads on high,
   and close the path to misery.

5. O come, O come, thou Lord of might,
   who to thy tribes on Sinai's height
   in ancient times didst give the Law,
   in cloud and majesty and awe.

162 O dearest Lord, thy sacred head

Henry Ernest Hardy (Father Andrew S.D.C.)
(1869-1946)

Vincent Novello (1781-1861)

ALBANO CM

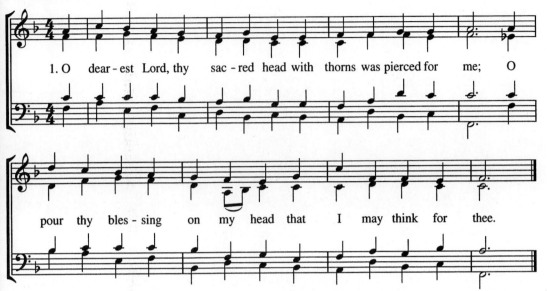

1. O dear - est Lord, thy sac - red head with thorns was pierced for me; O
pour thy bles - sing on my head that I may think for thee.

2. O dearest Lord, thy sacred hands
with nails were pierced for me;
O shed thy blessing on my hands
that they may work for thee.

3. O dearest Lord, thy sacred feet
with nails were pierced for me;
O pour thy blessing on my feet
that they may follow thee.

4. O dearest Lord, thy sacred heart
with spear was pierced for me;
O pour thy Spirit in my heart
that I may live for thee.

Cornelis Grootaers, Invention of a New Pyre Drawing Ltd.
European Publishing V. et al. and London Ltd.

163 O for a closer walk with God

William Cowper (1731-1800)

Melody from the 'Scottish Psalter' (1635)

CAITHNESS CM

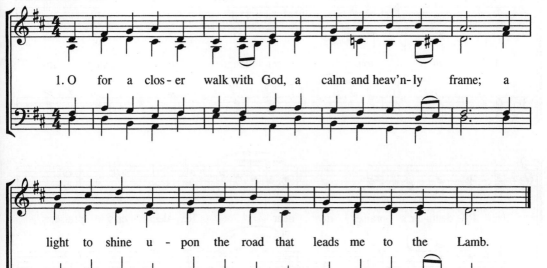

1. O for a clos-er walk with God, a calm and heav'n-ly frame; a
light to shine u - pon the road that leads me to the Lamb.

2. What peaceful hours I once enjoyed,
   how sweet their mem'ry still!
   But they have left an aching void
   the world can never fill.

3. The dearest idol I have known,
   whate'er that idol be,
   help me to tear it from thy throne,
   and worship only thee.

4. So shall my walk be close with God,
   calm and serene my frame;
   so purer light shall mark the road
   that leads me to the Lamb.

164 O for a thousand tongues to sing

Charles Wesley (1707-1788)

Thomas Jarman (1776-1861)

LYNGHAM 86 86 extended

1. O for a thou - sand tongues to sing my

dear Re- deem-er's praise, my dear Re - deem - er's praise,

the glo - ries of my God and King,

the

the tri - umphs of his grace, the tri - umphs of his

tri-umphs of his grace, the tri - umphs of his grace, the

grace, the tri - umphs of his grace!

tri - umphs of his grace, the tri - umphs of his grace!

2. Jesus! the name that charms our fears,
   that bids our sorrows cease;
   that bids our sorrows cease;
   'tis music in the sinner's ears,
   'tis life and health and peace. *(x3)*

3. He breaks the pow'r of cancelled sin,
   he sets the pris'ner free;
   he sets the pris'ner free;
   his blood can make the foulest clean;
   his blood availed for me. *(x3)*

4. He speaks; and, list'ning to his voice,
   new life the dead receive,
   new life the dead receive,
   the mournful broken hearts rejoice,
   the humble poor believe. *(x3)*

5. Hear him, ye deaf; his praise, ye dumb,
   your loosened tongues employ;
   your loosened tongues employ;
   ye blind, behold your Saviour come;
   and leap, ye lame, for joy! *(x3)*

6. My gracious Master and my God,
   assist me to proclaim
   assist me to proclaim
   and spread through all the earth abroad
   the honours of thy name. *(x3)*

165 Of the Father's love begotten

'Corde natus ex parentis' by
Aurelius Clemens Prudentius (348-413)
trans. John Mason Neale (1818-1866) alt.

Plainsong melody (13th century)
adapted by Theodoricus Petrus
in 'Piae Cantiones' (1582)

CORDE NATUS (DIVINUM MYSTERIUM) 87 87 87 7

1. Of the Fa - ther's love be - got - ten, ere the worlds be - gan to be, he is Al - pha and O - me - ga, he the source, the end - ing he, of the things that are, and have been, and that fu - ture years shall

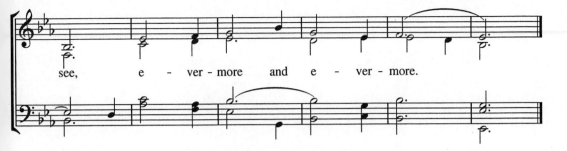

see, e - ver - more and e - ver - more.

2. At his word they were created;
   he commanded; it was done:
   heav'n and earth and depths of ocean
   in their threefold order one;
   all that grows beneath the shining
   of the light of moon and sun,
   evermore and evermore.

3. O that birth for ever blessèd,
   when the Virgin, full of grace,
   by the Holy Ghost conceiving,
   bore the Saviour of our race,
   and the babe, the world's Redeemer,
   first revealed his sacred face,
   evermore and evermore.

4. O ye heights of heav'n, adore him;
   angel hosts, his praises sing;
   pow'rs, dominions, bow before him,
   and extol our God and King:
   let no tongue on earth be silent,
   ev'ry voice in concert ring,
   evermore and evermore.

5. This is he whom seers and sages
   sang of old with one accord;
   whom the writings of the prophets
   promised in their faithful word;
   now he shines, the long-expected:
   let our songs declare his worth,
   evermore and evermore.

6. Christ, to thee, with God the Father,
   and, O Holy Ghost, to thee,
   hymn and chant and high thanksgiving,
   and unwearied praises be;
   honour, glory, and dominion,
   and eternal victory,
   evermore and evermore.

166 Oft in danger, oft in woe

Henry Kirke White (1785-1806)
and others

Henry John Gauntlett (1805-1876)

UNIVERSITY COLLEGE 77 77

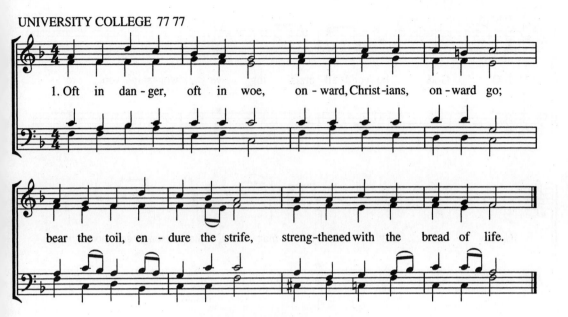

1. Oft in dan - ger, oft in woe, on - ward, Christ -ians, on - ward go;
bear the toil, en - dure the strife, streng-thened with the bread of life.

2. Onward through the desert night,
   keeping faith and vision bright;
   face the challenge of the hour
   trusting in your Saviour's pow'r.

3. Let not sorrow dim your eye,
   soon shall ev'ry tear be dry;
   let not fears your course impede,
   great your strength if great your need.

4. Let your drooping hearts be glad;
   march in faith and honour clad;
   march, nor think the journey long,
   march to hope's eternal song.

5. Onward, then, undaunted, move;
   more than faithful God will prove;
   though the raging waters flow,
   Christian pilgrims, onward go.

167 O God beyond all praising

Michael Perry (1942-1996)

Gustav Holst (1874-1934)

THAXTED 13 13 13 13 13 13

Unison

1. O God be-yond all prais - ing, we wor-ship you to -
day, and sing the love a -maz - ing that songs can-not re -
pay; for we can on-ly won - der at ev - 'ry gift you
send, at bles-sings with - out num - ber and mer-cies with - out
end: we lift our hearts be -fore you and wait up-on your

word,   we   hon - our and a - dore   you,   our   great and migh-ty   Lord.

2. Then hear, O gracious Saviour,
   accept the love we bring,
   that we who know your favour
   may serve you as our King;
   and whether our tomorrows
   be filled with good or ill,
   we'll triumph through our sorrows
   and rise to bless you still:
   to marvel at your beauty
   and glory in your ways,
   and make a joyful duty
   our sacrifice of praise.

168 O God, our help in ages past

Isaac Watts (1674-1748) alt.

William Croft (1678-1727)

ST ANNE CM

1. O God, our help in a - ges past, our hope for years to
come, our shel - ter from the stor - my blast, and our e - ter - nal home.

2. Beneath the shadow of thy throne,
   thy saints have dwelt secure;
   sufficient is thine arm alone,
   and our defence is sure.

3. Before the hills in order stood,
   or earth received her frame,
   from everlasting thou art God,
   to endless years the same.

4. A thousand ages in thy sight
   are like an evening gone;
   short as the watch that ends the night
   before the rising sun.

5. Time, like an ever-rolling stream,
   will bear us all away;
   we fade and vanish, as a dream
   dies at the op'ning day.

6. O God, our help in ages past,
   our hope for years to come,
   be thou our guard while troubles last,
   and our eternal home.

169 O happy band of pilgrims

John Mason Neale (1818-1866) alt.

Justin Heinrich Knecht (1752-1817)

KNECHT (KOCHER) 76 76

1. O hap-py band of pil-grims, if on-ward ye will tread, with
Je - sus as your fel - low, to Je - sus as your head.

2. The cross that Jesus carried
   he carried as your due:
   the crown that Jesus weareth
   he weareth it for you.

3. The faith by which ye see him,
   the hope in which ye yearn,
   the love that through all troubles
   to him alone will turn.

4. What are they but forerunners
   to lead you to his sight,
   the longed-for distant dawning
   of uncreated light?

5. The trials that beset you,
   the sorrows ye endure,
   are known to Christ your Saviour,
   whose perfect grace will cure.

6. O happy band of pilgrims,
   let fear not dim your eyes,
   remember, your afflictions
   shall lead to such a prize!

170 O Jesus, I have promised

John Ernest Bode (1816-1874) William Harold Ferguson (1874-1950)

TUNE 1: WOLVERCOTE 76 76 D

1. O Jesus, I have promised to serve thee to the end; be thou for ever near me, my Master and my friend: I shall not fear the battle if thou art by my side, nor wander from the pathway if thou wilt be my guide.

2. O let me feel thee near me:
   the world is ever near;
   I see the sights that dazzle,
   the tempting sounds I hear;
   my foes are ever near me,
   around me and within;
   but, Jesus, draw thou nearer,
   and shield my soul from sin.

3. O let me hear thee speaking
   in accents clear and still,
   above the storms of passion,
   the murmurs of self-will;
   O speak to reassure me,
   to hasten or control;
   O speak and make me listen,
   thou guardian of my soul.

4. O Jesus, thou hast promised,
   to all who follow thee,
   that where thou art in glory
   there shall thy servant be;
   and, Jesus, I have promised
   to serve thee to the end:
   O give me grace to follow,
   my Master and my friend.

5. O let me see thy foot-marks,
   and in them plant mine own;
   my hope to follow duly
   is in thy strength alone:
   O guide me, call me, draw me,
   uphold me to the end;
   and then in heav'n receive me,
   my Saviour and my friend.

John Ernest Bode (1816-1874)

Geoffrey Beaumont (1903-1970)
arr. Norman Warren

TUNE 2: HATHEROP CASTLE 76 76 D

1. O Jesus, I have promised to serve thee to the end;
be thou for ever near me, my Master and my friend:
I shall not fear the battle if thou art by my side, nor
wander from the pathway if thou wilt be my guide.

friend, and then in heav'n re - ceive me, my Sa - viour and my friend.

2. O let me feel thee near me:
   the world is ever near;
   I see the sights that dazzle,
   the tempting sounds I hear;
   my foes are ever near me,
   around me and within;
   but, Jesus, draw thou nearer,
   and shield my soul from sin.

3. O let me hear thee speaking
   in accents clear and still,
   above the storms of passion,
   the murmurs of self-will;
   O speak to reassure me,
   to hasten or control;
   O speak and make me listen,
   thou guardian of my soul.

4. O Jesus, thou hast promised,
   to all who follow thee,
   that where thou art in glory
   there shall thy servant be;
   and, Jesus, I have promised
   to serve thee to the end:
   O give me grace to follow,
   my Master and my friend.

5. O let me see thy foot-marks,
   and in them plant mine own;
   my hope to follow duly
   is in thy strength alone:
   O guide me, call me, draw me,
   uphold me to the end;
   and then in heav'n receive me,
   my Saviour and my friend.

171 O little town of Bethlehem

Phillips Brooks (1835-1893) alt.

Traditional English melody collected and
arr. Ralph Vaughan Williams (1872-1958)

FOREST GREEN DCM

1. O lit-tle town of Beth-le-hem, how still we see thee lie! A-bove thy deep and dream-less sleep the si-lent stars go by. Yet in thy dark streets shi-neth the e-ver-last-ing light; the hopes and fears of all the years are met in thee to-night.

2. O morning stars, together
proclaim the holy birth,
and praises sing to God the King,
and peace to all the earth;
For Christ is born of Mary;
and, gathered all above,
while mortals sleep, the angels keep
their watch of wond'ring love.

3. How silently, how silently,
the wondrous gift is giv'n!
So God imparts to human hearts
the blessings of his heav'n.
No ear may hear his coming;
but in this world of sin,
where meek souls will receive him, still
the dear Christ enters in.

4. O holy child of Bethlehem,
descend to us, we pray;
cast out our sin, and enter in,
be born in us today.
We hear the Christmas angels
the great glad tidings tell:
O come to us, abide with us,
our Lord Emmanuel.

172 O Lord, my God

How great thou art

Stuart K. Hine (1899-1989)

Swedish folk melody
arr. Stuart K. Hine

HOW GREAT THOU ART 11 10 11 10 and Refrain

1. O Lord, my God! when I in awe-some won-der con-si-der

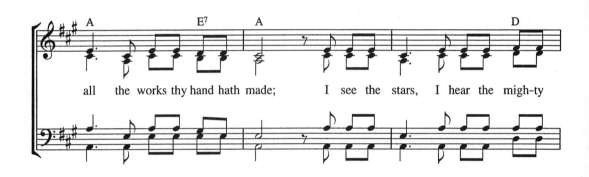

all the works thy hand hath made; I see the stars, I hear the migh-ty

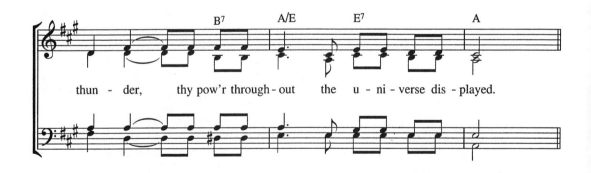

thun-der, thy pow'r through-out the u-ni-verse dis-played.

Refrain

Then sings my soul, my Sa-viour God, to thee, how great thou

art!   how great thou art!   Then sings my   soul,   my Sa-viour God, to

thee,   how great thou art!   how great thou   art!

2. When through the woods and forest glades I wander
and hear the birds sing sweetly in the trees;
when I look down from lofty mountain grandeur,
and hear the brook, and feel the gentle breeze.

3. And when I think that God, his Son not sparing,
sent him to die, I scarce can take it in:
that on the cross, my burden gladly bearing,
he bled and died to take away my sin.

4. When Christ shall come with shout of acclamation
and take me home, what joy shall fill my heart!
Then shall I bow in humble adoration,
and there proclaim, my God how great thou art!

173 O Love that wilt not let me go

George Matheson (1842-1906)   Albert Lister Peace (1844-1912)

ST MARGARET 88 88 6

1. O Love that wilt not let me go, I rest my wea-ry soul in thee; I give thee back the life I owe, that in thine o-cean depths its flow may rich - er, full - er be.

2. O Light that follow'st all my way,
   I yield my flick'ring torch to thee;
   my heart restores its borrowed ray,
   that in thy sunshine's blaze its day
   may brighter, fairer be.

3. O Joy that seekest me through pain,
   I cannot close my heart to thee;
   I trace the rainbow through the rain,
   and feel the promise is not vain
   that morn shall tearless be.

4. O Cross that liftest up my head,
   I dare not ask to fly from thee:
   I lay in dust life's glory dead,
   and from the ground there blossoms red
   life that shall endless be.

174 On a hill far away

The old rugged cross

George Bennard

George Bennard (1873-1958)

THE OLD RUGGED CROSS 66 8 D and Refrain

1. On a hill far a-way stood an old rug-ged cross, the em-blem of suff-'ring and shame; and I loved that old cross where the dear-est and best for a world of lost sin-ners was slain. So I'll cher-ish the old rug-ged cross, till my tro-phies at last I lay

down; I will cling to the old rug - ged cross

and ex - change it some day for a crown.

2. O that old rugged cross,
   so despised by the world,
   has a wondrous attraction for me:
   for the dear Lamb of God
   left his glory above
   to bear it to dark Calvary.

3. In the old rugged cross,
   stained with blood so divine,
   a wondrous beauty I see.
   For 'twas on that old cross
   Jesus suffered and died
   to pardon and sanctify me.

4. To the old rugged cross
   I will ever be true,
   its shame and reproach gladly bear.
   Then he'll call me some day
   to my home far away;
   there his glory for ever I'll share.

175 Once in royal David's city

Cecil Frances Alexander (1818-1895) alt.

Henry John Gauntlett (1805-1876)

IRBY 87 87 77

1. Once in royal David's city stood a lowly cattle shed, where a mother laid her baby in a manger for his bed: Mary was that mother mild, Jesus Christ her little child.

2. He came down to earth from heaven,
who is God and Lord of all,
and his shelter was a stable,
and his cradle was a stall;
with the needy, poor and lowly,
lived on earth our Saviour holy.

3. For he is our childhood's pattern,
day by day like us he grew;
he was little, weak and helpless,
tears and smiles like us he knew;
and he feeleth for our sadness,
and he shareth in our gladness.

4. And our eyes at last shall see him
through his own redeeming love,
for that child so dear and gentle
is our Lord in heav'n above;
and he leads his children on
to the place where he is gone.

176 Once, only once, and once for all

William Bright (1824-1901)　　　　　　　　　Vincent Novello (1781-1861)

ALBANO CM

1. Once, on - ly once, and once for all, his pre-cious life he gave; be -
fore the Cross our spi - rits fall, and own it strong to save.

2. 'One off'ring, single and complete,'
   with lips and heart we say;
   but what he never can repeat
   he shows forth day by day.

3. For, as the priest of Aaron's line
   within the holiest stood,
   and sprinkled all the mercy-shrine
   with sacrificial blood;

4. So he who once atonement wrought,
   our Priest of endless pow'r,
   presents himself for those he bought
   in that dark noontide hour.

5. And so we show thy death, O Lord,
   till thou again appear;
   and feel, when we approach thy board,
   we have an altar here.

6. All glory to the Father be,
   all glory to the Son,
   all glory, Holy Ghost, to thee,
   while endless ages run.

177 On Christmas night all Christians sing

Traditional English carol, alt.

Traditional English melody collected and
arr. Ralph Vaughan Williams (1872-1958)

SUSSEX CAROL 88 88 88

Unison

1. On Christ - mas night all Christ - ians sing, to hear the news the an - gels bring, on Christ - mas night all Christ - ians sing, to hear the news the an - gels bring, news of great joy, news of great mirth, news of our mer - ci - ful King's birth.

2. Then why should we on earth be so sad,
   since our Redeemer made us glad,
   then why should we on earth be so sad,
   since our Redeemer made us glad,
   when from our sin he set us free,
   all for to gain our liberty?

3. When sin departs before his grace,
   then life and health come in its place,
   when sin departs before his grace,
   then life and health come in its place,
   angels and earth with joy may sing,
   all for to see the new-born King.

4. All out of darkness we have light,
   which made the angels sing this night:
   all out of darkness we have light,
   which made the angels sing this night:
   'Glory to God and peace to men,
   now and for evermore. Amen.'

178 One more step along the world I go

Sydney Carter

Sydney Carter (b.1915)
arr. Colin Hand

SOUTHCOTE 99 79 and Refrain

1. One more step a-long the world I go, one more step a-long the world I go. From the old things to the new keep me tra-vel-ling a-long with you. And it's from the old I tra-vel to the new, keep me tra-vel-ling a-long with you.

2. Round the corners of the world I turn,
   more and more about the world I learn.
   All the new things that I see
   you'll be looking at along with me.

3. As I travel through the bad and good,
   keep me travelling the way I should.
   Where I see no way to go,
   you'll be telling me the way, I know.

4. Give me courage when the world is rough,
   keep me loving though the world is tough.
   Leap and sing in all I do,
   keep me travelling along with you.

5. You are older than the world can be,
   you are younger than the life in me.
   Ever old and ever new,
   keep me travelling along with you.

179 On this day, the first of days

18th century
trans. Henry Williams Baker (1821-1877)
adapted by the editors of 'English Praise'

Freylinghausen's 'Gesangbuch' (1704)

LÜBECK (GOTT SEI DANK) 77 77

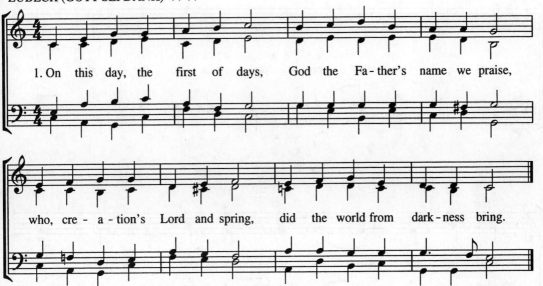

1. On this day, the first of days, God the Fa-ther's name we praise, who, cre - a - tion's Lord and spring, did the world from dark - ness bring.

2. On this day his only Son
over death the triumph won;
on this day the Spirit came
with his gifts of living flame.

3. On this day his people raise
one pure sacrifice of praise,
and, with all the saints above,
tell of Christ's redeeming love.

4. Praise, O God, to thee be giv'n,
praise on earth and praise in heav'n,
praise to thy eternal Son,
who this day our vict'ry won.

180 O praise ye the Lord!

Henry Williams Baker (1821-1877)
based on Psalms 148 and 150 alt.

Charles Hubert Hastings Parry (1848-1918)

LAUDATE DOMINUM (PARRY) 10 10 11 11

1. O praise ye the Lord! praise him in the height; re -

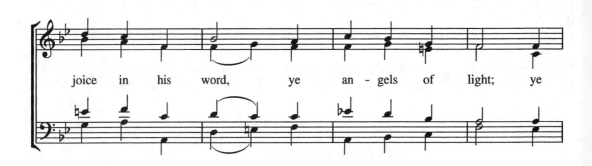

joice in his word, ye an - gels of light; ye

hea - vens, a - dore him, by whom ye were made, and

wor - ship be - fore him, in bright - ness ar - rayed.

2. O praise ye the Lord! praise him upon earth,
   in tuneful accord, all you of new birth;
   praise him who hath brought you his grace from above,
   praise him who hath taught you to sing of his love.

3. O praise ye the Lord! all things that give sound;
   each jubilant chord re-echo around;
   loud organs his glory forth tell in deep tone,
   and, sweet harp, the story of what he hath done.

4. O praise ye the Lord! thanksgiving and song
   to him be outpoured all ages along:
   for love in creation, for heaven restored,
   for grace of salvation, O praise ye the Lord!

181 O sacred head sore wounded

Paul Gerhardt (1607-1676) based on 'Salve caput cruentatum'
trans. Robert Bridges (1844-1930)

Hans Leo Hassler (1564-1612)
harm. Johann Sebastian Bach (1685-1750)

PASSION CHORALE 76 76 D

1. O sa - cred head sore wound - ed, de - filed and put to scorn; O king - ly head sur - round - ed with mock - ing crown of thorn: what sor - row mars thy gran - deur? Can death thy bloom de - flower? O

coun - ten - ance whose splen - dour the hosts of heav'n a - dore.

2. Thy beauty, long-desirèd,
   hath vanished from our sight;
   thy pow'r is all expirèd,
   and quenched the light of light.
   Ah me, for whom thou diest,
   hide not so far thy grace:
   show me, O love most highest,
   the brightness of thy face.

3. I pray thee, Jesus, own me,
   me, shepherd good, for thine;
   who to thy fold hast won me,
   and fed with truth divine.
   Me guilty, me refuse not,
   incline thy face to me,
   this comfort that I lose not,
   on earth to comfort thee.

4. In thy most bitter passion
   my heart to share doth cry,
   with thee for my salvation
   upon the cross to die.
   Ah, keep my heart thus movèd,
   to stand thy cross beneath,
   to mourn thee, well-belovèd,
   yet thank thee for thy death.

5. My days are few, O fail not,
   with thine immortal power,
   to hold me that I quail not
   in death's most fearful hour:
   that I may fight befriended,
   and see in my last strife
   to me thine arms extended
   upon the cross of life.

182 O strength and stay

St Ambrose (c.340-397)
trans. John Ellerton (1826-1893)
and Fenton John Anthony Hort (1828-1892)

John Bacchus Dykes (1823-1876)

STRENGTH AND STAY 11 10 11 10

1. O strength and stay up - hold - ing all cre - a - tion,
who e - ver dost thy - self un - moved a - bide,
yet day by day the light in due gra - da - tion
from hour to hour through all its chan - ges guide.

2. Grant to life's day a calm unclouded ending,
an eve untouched by shadows of decay,
the brightness of a holy death-bed blending
with dawning glories of th'eternal day.

3. Hear us, O Father, gracious and forgiving,
through Jesus Christ thy co-eternal Word,
who with the Holy Ghost by all things living
now and to endless ages art adored.

183 O thou who camest from above

Charles Wesley (1707-1788)
based on Leviticus 6:13

Samuel Sebastian Wesley (1810-1876)

HEREFORD LM

1. O thou who cam - est from a - bove the fire ce -
les - tial to im - part, kin - dle a flame of
sac - red love on the mean al - tar of my heart.

2. There let it for thy glory burn
   with inextinguishable blaze,
   and trembling to its source return
   in humble prayer and fervent praise.

3. Jesus, confirm my heart's desire
   to work and speak and think for thee;
   still let me guard the holy fire
   and still stir up the gift in me.

4. Ready for all thy perfect will,
   my acts of faith and love repeat,
   till death thy endless mercies seal,
   and make the sacrifice complete.

184 O worship the King

Robert Grant (1779-1838)
based on Psalm 104

Melody and bass by William Croft (1678-1727)
in 'A Supplement to the New Version' (1708)

HANOVER 10 10 11 11

1. O worship the King all glorious above;
O gratefully sing his pow'r and his love:
our shield and defender, the Ancient of Days,
pavilioned in splendour, and girded with praise.

2. O tell of his might, O sing of his grace,
whose robe is the light, whose canopy space;
his chariots of wrath the deep thunder-clouds form,
and dark is his path on the wings of the storm.

3. This earth, with its store of wonders untold,
almighty, thy pow'r hath founded of old.
hath stablished it fast by a changeless decree,
and round it hath cast, like a mantle, the sea.

4. Thy bountiful care what tongue can recite?
It breathes in the air, it shines in the light;
it streams from the hills, it descends to the plain,
and sweetly distils in the dew and the rain.

5. Frail children of dust, and feeble as frail,
in thee do we trust, nor find thee to fail;
thy mercies how tender, how firm to the end!
Our maker, defender, redeemer, and friend.

6. O measureless might, ineffable love,
while angels delight to hymn thee above,
thy humbler creation, though feeble their lays,
with true adoration shall sing to thy praise.

185 O worship the Lord in the beauty of holiness

John Samuel Bewley Monsell (1811-1875)

Melody from the 'Rheinhardt MS',
Üttingen (1754)

WAS LEBET 13 10 13 10

1. O worship the Lord in the beauty of holiness;
bow down before him, his glory proclaim; with
gold of obedience and incense of lowliness,
kneel and adore him: the Lord is his name.

2. Low at his feet lay thy burden of carefulness:
high on his heart he will bear it for thee,
comfort thy sorrows, and answer thy prayerfulness,
guiding thy steps as may best for thee be.

3. Fear not to enter his courts in the slenderness
of the poor wealth thou wouldst reckon as thine:
truth in its beauty, and love in its tenderness,
these are the off'rings to lay on his shrine.

4. These, though we bring them in trembling and fearfulness,
he will accept for the name that is dear;
mornings of joy give for evenings of tearfulness,
trust for our trembling and hope for our fear.

186 Peace, perfect peace, is the gift

Kevin Mayhew

Kevin Mayhew (b.1942)

2. Love, perfect love, is the gift of Christ our Lord. *(x2)*
Thus, says the Lord, will the world know my friends.
Love, perfect love, is the gift of Christ our Lord.

3. Faith, perfect faith, is the gift of Christ our Lord. *(x2)*
Thus, says the Lord, will the world know my friends.
Faith, perfect faith, is the gift of Christ our Lord.

4. Hope, perfect hope, is the gift of Christ our Lord. *(x2)*
Thus, says the Lord, will the world know my friends.
Hope perfect hope, is the gift of Christ our Lord.

5. Joy, perfect joy, is the gift of Christ our Lord. *(x2)*
Thus, says the Lord, will the world know my friends.
Joy, perfect joy, is the gift of Christ our Lord.

187 Praise him

Unknown

Unknown
arr. Christopher Tambling

1. Praise him, praise him, praise him in the morn-ing, praise him in the noon-time. Praise him, praise him, praise him when the sun goes down.

2. Love him, love him,
   love him in the morning,
   love him in the noontime.
   Love him, love him,
   love him when the sun goes down.

3. Trust him, trust him,
   trust him in the morning,
   trust him in the noontime.
   Trust him, trust him,
   trust him when the sun goes down.

4. Serve him, serve him,
   serve him in the morning,
   serve him in the noontime.
   Serve him, serve him,
   serve him when the sun goes down.

5. Jesus, Jesus,
   Jesus in the morning,
   Jesus in the noontime.
   Jesus, Jesus,
   Jesus when the sun goes down.

188 Praise, my soul, the King of heaven

Henry Francis Lyte (1793-1847)
based on Psalm 103

John Goss (1800-1880)

PRAISE, MY SOUL 87 87 87

Unison

1. Praise, my soul, the King of hea - ven! To his feet thy tri - bute bring; ran - somed, healed, re - stored, for - giv - en, who like me his praise should sing? Praise him! Praise him! Praise him! Praise him! Praise the e - ver - last - ing King!

2. Praise him for his grace and fa - vour to our fa - thers in dis - tress; praise him still the same as e - ver, slow to chide and swift to bless. Praise him! Praise him! Praise him! Praise him! Glo - rious in his faith - ful - ness!

Unison

3. Fa - ther - like, he tends and spares us; well our fee - ble

frame he knows; in his hands he gent - ly bears us,

res - cues us from all our foes. Praise him! Praise him!

Praise him! Praise him! Wide - ly as his mer - cy flows!

4. An - gels, help us to a - dore him; ye be - hold him face to face; sun and moon, bow down be - fore him, dwell - ers all in time and space. Praise him! Praise him! Praise him! Praise him! Praise with us the God of grace!

189 Praise the Lord, ye heavens, adore him

vs. 1, 2: from 'Foundling Hospital Collection' (1796)
v.3: Edward Osler (1798-1863)

Croatian Folk melody adapted by
Franz Joseph Haydn (1732-1809)

AUSTRIA 87 87 D

1. Praise the Lord, ye heav'ns, a-dore him! Praise him, an-gels, in the height; sun and moon, re-joice be-fore him, praise him, all ye stars and light. Praise the Lord, for he hath spo-ken; worlds his migh-ty voice o-beyed: laws, which ne-ver shall be bro-ken, for their gui-dance he hath made.

2. Praise the Lord, for he is glorious:
   never shall his promise fail.
   God hath made his saints victorious;
   sin and death shall not prevail.
   Praise the God of our salvation,
   hosts on high, his pow'r proclaim;
   heav'n and earth and all creation,
   laud and magnify his name!

3. Worship, honour, glory, blessing,
   Lord, we offer to thy name;
   young and old, thy praise expressing,
   join their Saviour to proclaim.
   As the saints in heav'n adore thee,
   we would bow before thy throne;
   as thine angels serve before thee,
   so on earth thy will be done.

190 Praise to the Holiest

John Henry Newman (1801-1890)

Melody adapted from
Thomas Haweis (1734-1820)

TUNE 1: RICHMOND CM

1. Praise to the Ho - liest in the height, and in the depth be praise: in all his words most won - der - ful, most sure in all his ways.

2. O loving wisdom of our God!
   when all was sin and shame,
   a second Adam to the fight,
   and to the rescue came.

3. O wisest love! that flesh and blood,
   which did in Adam fail,
   should strive afresh against the foe,
   should strive and should prevail.

4. And that a higher gift than grace
   should flesh and blood refine,
   God's presence and his very self,
   and essence all divine.

5. And in the garden secretly,
   and on the cross on high,
   should teach his brethren, and inspire
   to suffer and to die.

6. Praise to the Holiest in the height,
   and in the depth be praise;
   in all his words most wonderful,
   most sure in all his ways.

John Henry Newman (1801-1890)

John Bacchus Dykes (1823-1876)

TUNE 2: GERONTIUS CM

1. Praise to the Ho - liest in the height, and in the depth be praise; in all his words most won - der - ful, most sure in all his ways.

191 Praise to the Lord, the Almighty

Joachim Neander (1650-1680)

From 'Praxis Pietatis Melica' (1668)

trans. Catherine Winkworth (1827-1878)

LOBE DEN HERREN 14 14 4 7 8

1. Praise to the Lord, the Al - migh - ty, the King of cre -

a - tion! O my soul, praise him, for he is thy

health and sal - va - tion. All ye who hear, now to his

tem - ple draw near; join-ing in glad a - do - ra - tion.

2. Praise to the Lord, who o'er all things so wondrously reigneth,
   shieldeth thee gently from harm, or when fainting sustaineth:
   hast thou not seen
   how thy heart's wishes have been
   granted in what he ordaineth?

3. Praise to the Lord, who doth prosper thy work and defend thee,
   surely his goodness and mercy shall daily attend thee:
   ponder anew
   what the Almighty can do,
   if to the end he befriend thee.

4. Praise to the Lord, O let all that is in us adore him!
   All that hath life and breath, come now with praises before him.
   Let the 'Amen'
   sound from his people again,
   gladly for ay we adore him.

192 Put thou thy trust in God

Paul Gerhardt (1607-1676)
trans. John Wesley (1703-1791) and others

Samuel Wesley (1766-1837)

DONCASTER SM

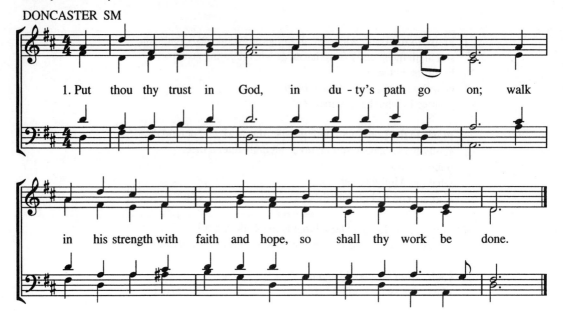

1. Put thou thy trust in God, in du-ty's path go on; walk in his strength with faith and hope, so shall thy work be done.

2. Commit thy ways to him,
   thy works into his hands,
   and rest on his unchanging word,
   who heav'n and earth commands.

3. Though years on years roll on,
   his cov'nant shall endure;
   though clouds and darkness hide his path,
   the promised grace is sure.

4. Give to the winds thy fears;
   hope, and be undismayed:
   God hears thy sighs and counts thy tears;
   God shall lift up thy head.

5. Through waves and clouds and storms
   his pow'r will clear thy way:
   wait thou his time; the darkest night
   shall end in brightest day.

6. Leave to his sov'reign sway
   to choose and to command;
   so shalt thou, wond'ring, own his way,
   how wise, how strong his hand.

193 Rejoice, O land, in God thy might

Robert Bridges (1844-1930)

William Knapp (1698-1768)

WAREHAM LM

1. Re - joice, O land, in God thy might; his will o - bey, him serve a - right; for thee the saints up - lift their voice: fear not, O land, in God re - joice.

2. Glad shalt thou be, with blessing crowned,
with joy and peace thou shalt abound;
yea, love with thee shall make his home
until thou see God's kingdom come.

3. He shall forgive thy sins untold:
remember thou his love of old;
walk in his way, his word adore,
and keep his truth for evermore.

194 Rejoice, the Lord is King

Charles Wesley (1707-1788)

George Frideric Handel (1685-1759)

GOPSAL 66 66 and Refrain

1. Re - joice, the Lord is King! Your Lord and King a -
dore; mor - tals, give thanks and sing, and
tri - umph e - ver - more. Lift up your heart, lift
up your voice; re - joice, a - gain I say, re - joice.

2. Jesus the Saviour reigns,
   the God of truth and love;
   when he had purged our stains,
   he took his seat above.

3. His kingdom cannot fail;
   he rules o'er earth and heav'n;
   the keys of death and hell
   are to our Jesus giv'n.

4. He sits at God's right hand
   till all his foes submit,
   and bow to his command,
   and fall beneath his feet.

195 Ride on, ride on in majesty

Henry Hart Milman (1791-1868) alt.

From 'Musikalisches Handbuch' (1690)

WINCHESTER NEW LM

1. Ride on, ride on in ma-jes-ty! Hark, all the tribes ho-san-na cry; thy hum-ble beast pur-sues his road with palms and scat-tered gar-ments strowed.

2. Ride on, ride on in majesty!
   In lowly pomp ride on to die;
   O Christ, thy triumphs now begin
   o'er captive death and conquered sin.

3. Ride on, ride on in majesty!
   The wingèd squadrons of the sky
   look down with sad and wond'ring eyes
   to see th'approaching sacrifice.

4. Ride on, ride on in majesty!
   Thy last and fiercest strife is nigh;
   the Father, on his sapphire throne,
   awaits his own appointed Son.

5. Ride on, ride on in majesty!
   In lowly pomp ride on to die;
   bow thy meek head to mortal pain,
   then take, O God, thy pow'r, and reign.

196 Rock of ages

Augustus Montague Toplady (1740-1778) alt.

Richard Redhead (1820-1901)

PETRA (REDHEAD NO. 76) 77 77 77

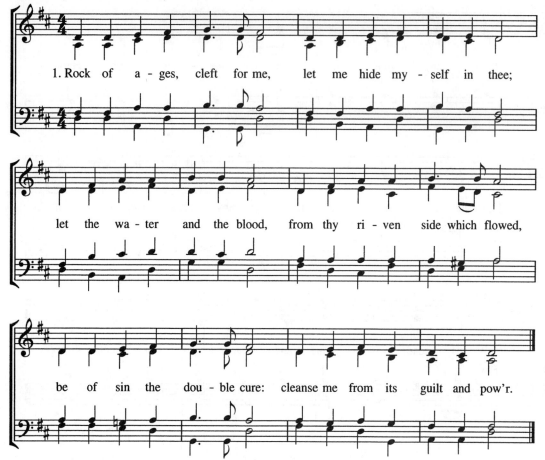

1. Rock of a - ges, cleft for me, let me hide my - self in thee; let the wa - ter and the blood, from thy ri - ven side which flowed, be of sin the dou - ble cure: cleanse me from its guilt and pow'r.

2. Not the labours of my hands
   can fulfil thy law's demands;
   could my zeal no respite know,
   could my tears for ever flow,
   all for sin could not atone:
   thou must save, and thou alone.

3. Nothing in my hands I bring,
   simply to the cross I cling;
   naked, come to thee for dress;
   helpless, look to thee for grace;
   tainted, to the fountain fly;
   wash me, Saviour, or I die.

4. While I draw this fleeting breath,
   when mine eyelids close in death,
   when I soar through tracts unknown,
   see thee on thy judgement throne;
   Rock of ages, cleft for me,
   let me hide myself in thee.

197 Saviour, again to thy dear name we raise

John Ellerton (1826-1893)   Edward John Hopkins (1818-1901)

ELLERS 10 10 10 10

1. Saviour, again to thy dear name we raise
with one accord our parting hymn of praise;
we stand to bless thee ere our worship cease;
then, lowly kneeling, wait thy word of peace.

2. Grant us thy peace upon our homeward way;
with thee began, with thee shall end, the day:
guard thou the lips from sin, the hearts from shame,
that in this house have called upon thy name.

3. Grant us thy peace, Lord, through the coming night;
turn thou for us its darkness into light;
from harm and danger keep thy children free,
for dark and light are both alike to thee.

4. Grant us thy peace throughout our earthly life,
our balm in sorrow, and our stay in strife;
then, when thy voice shall bid our conflict cease,
call us, O Lord, to thine eternal peace.

198 See, amid the winter's snow

Edward Caswall (1814-1878)

John Goss (1800-1880)

HUMILITY (OXFORD) 77 77 and Refrain

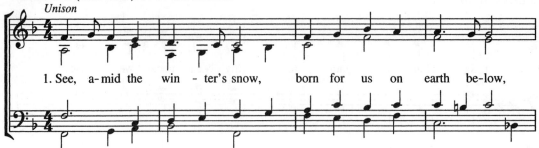

1. See, a-mid the win – ter's snow, born for us on earth be-low,

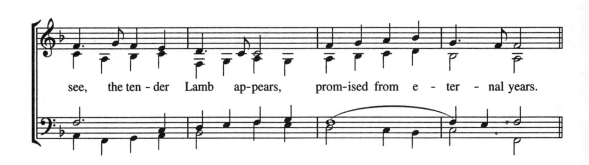

see, the ten – der Lamb ap-pears, prom-ised from e – ter – nal years.

Refrain
Harmony

Hail, thou e – ver – bles-sed morn, hail, re-demp-tion's hap – py dawn!

Sing through all Je – ru – sa-lem, Christ is born in Beth – le – hem.

2. Lo, within a manger lies
   he who built the starry skies;
   he who, throned in heights sublime,
   sits amid the cherubim.

3. Say, you holy shepherds, say,
   what your joyful news today?
   Wherefore have you left your sheep
   on the lonely mountain steep?

4. 'As we watched at dead of night,
   there appeared a wondrous light;
   angels, singing peace on earth,
   told us of the Saviour's birth.'

5. Sacred infant, all divine,
   what a tender love was thine,
   thus to come from highest bliss,
   down to such a world as this!

6. Virgin mother, Mary, blest,
   by the joys that fill thy breast,
   pray for us, that we may prove
   worthy of the Saviour's love.

199 See him lying on a bed of straw

Michael Perry

CALYPSO CAROL Irregular and Refrain

Michael Perry (1942-1996)
arr. Christopher Tambling

1. See him ly-ing on a bed of straw: a draugh-ty sta-ble with an o-pen door.

Ma-ry cra-dl-ing the babe she bore: the Prince of Glo-ry is his name.

Refrain

O now car-ry me to Beth-le-hem to see the Lord of love a-gain:

To verses

just as poor as was the sta-ble then, the Prince of Glo-ry when he came!

Last time

sta-ble then, the Prince of Glo-ry when he came!

2. Star of silver, sweep across the skies,
   show where Jesus in the manger lies;
   shepherds, swiftly from your stupor rise
   to see the Saviour of the world!

3. Angels, sing again the song you sang,
   sing the glory of God's gracious plan;
   sing that Bethlehem's little baby can
   be the Saviour of us all.

4. Mine are riches, from your poverty;
   from your innocence, eternity;
   mine, forgiveness by your death for me,
   child of sorrow for my joy.

200 Silent night

Joseph Mohr (1792-1848)
trans. John Freeman Young (1820-1885)

Franz Grüber (1787-1863)
arr. Colin Hand

STILLE NACHT Irregular

2. Silent night, holy night.
   Shepherds quake at the sight,
   glories stream from heaven afar,
   heav'nly hosts sing alleluia:
   Christ, the Saviour is born,
   Christ, the Saviour is born.

3. Silent night, holy night.
   Son of God, love's pure light,
   radiant beams from thy holy face,
   with the dawn of redeeming grace:
   Jesus, Lord, at thy birth,
   Jesus, Lord, at thy birth.

201 Soldiers of Christ, arise

Charles Wesley (1707-1788)
based on Ephesians 6:10-18

William Henry Monk (1823-1889)

ST ETHELWALD SM

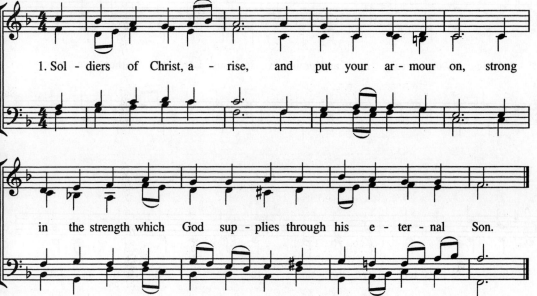

1. Sol - diers of Christ, a - rise, and put your ar - mour on, strong
in the strength which God sup - plies through his e - ter - nal Son.

2. Strong in the Lord of hosts,
   and in his mighty pow'r;
   who in the strength of Jesus trusts
   is more than conqueror.

3. Stand then in his great might,
   with all his strength endued;
   and take, to arm you for the fight,
   the panoply of God.

4. To keep your armour bright,
   attend with constant care,
   still walking in your Captain's sight
   and watching unto prayer.

5. From strength to strength go on,
   wrestle and fight and pray;
   tread all the pow'rs of darkness down,
   and win the well-fought day.

6. That, having all things done,
   and all your conflicts past,
   ye may o'ercome, through Christ alone,
   and stand entire at last.

202 Songs of thankfulness and praise

Christopher Wordsworth (1807-1885)

Charles Steggall (1826-1905)

ST EDMUND 77 77 D

1. Songs of thank-ful-ness and praise, Je-sus, Lord, to thee we raise,

ma-ni-fes-ted by the star to the sa-ges from a-far;

branch of roy-al Da-vid's stem, in thy birth at Beth-le-hem;

an-thems be to thee ad-dressed: God in man made ma-ni-fest.

2. Manifest at Jordan's stream,
   prophet, priest and King supreme,
   and at Cana wedding-guest,
   in thy Godhead manifest,
   manifest in pow'r divine,
   changing water into wine;
   anthems be to thee addressed:
   God in man made manifest.

3. Manifest in making whole,
   palsied limbs and fainting soul,
   manifest in valiant fight,
   quelling all the devil's might,
   manifest in gracious will,
   ever bringing good from ill;
   anthems be to thee addressed:
   God in man made manifest.

4. Sun and moon shall darkened be,
   stars shall fall, the heav'ns shall flee;
   Christ will then like lightning shine,
   all will see his glorious sign.
   All will then the trumpet hear,
   all will see the judge appear;
   thou by all wilt be confessed:
   God in man made manifest.

5. Grant us grace to see thee, Lord,
   mirrored in thy holy word;
   may we imitate thee now,
   and be pure, as pure art thou;
   that we like to thee may be
   at thy great Epiphany,
   and may praise thee, ever blest,
   God in man made manifest.

203 Spirit of the living God

Daniel Iverson

Daniel Iverson (1890-1972)

LIVING GOD 75 75 44 75

1. Spirit of the living God, fall afresh on me.
Spirit of the living God, fall afresh on me.
Melt me, mould me, fill me, use me.
Spirit of the living God, fall afresh on me.

2. Spirit of the living God, fall afresh on us.
Spirit of the living God, fall afresh on us.
Melt us, mould us, fill us, use us.
Spirit of the living God, fall afresh on us.

When appropriate, a third verse may be added,
singing 'on them', for example, before Confirmation,
or at a service for the sick.

204 Stand up and bless the Lord

James Montgomery (1771-1854)   Charles Lockhart (1745-1815)

CARLISLE SM

1. Stand up and bless the Lord, ye people of his choice; stand up and bless the Lord your God with heart and soul and voice.

2. Though high above all praise,
   above all blessing high,
   who would not fear his holy name,
   and laud and magnify?

3. O for the living flame
   from his own altar brought,
   to touch our lips, our mind inspire,
   and wing to heav'n our thought.

4. God is our strength and song,
   and his salvation ours;
   then be his love in Christ proclaimed
   with all our ransomed pow'rs.

5. Stand up and bless the Lord,
   the Lord your God adore;
   stand up and bless his glorious name
   henceforth for evermore.

205 Stand up, stand up for Jesus

Jean Holloway (b.1939)   George James Webb (1803-1887)

MORNING LIGHT 76 76 D

1. Stand up, stand up for Je - sus, stand up be - fore his cross, an in - stru - ment of tor - ture in - flic - ting pain and loss; trans - formed by his o - be - dience to God's re - dee - ming plan, the cross was o - ver - pow - ered by Christ, both God and man.

2. Stand up, stand up for Jesus,
   be counted as his own;
   his gospel of forgiveness
   he cannot spread alone.
   The love which draws us to him,
   he calls us out to share;
   he calls us to the margins
   to be his presence there.

3. Stand up, stand up for Jesus,
   in faith and hope be strong,
   stand firm for right and justice,
   opposed to sin and wrong.
   Give comfort to the wounded,
   and care for those in pain,
   for Christ, in those who suffer,
   is crucified again.

4. Stand up, stand up for Jesus,
   who reigns as King of kings,
   be ready for the challenge
   of faith his kingship brings.
   He will not force obedience,
   he gives to each the choice
   to turn from all that's holy,
   or in his love rejoice.

5. Stand up, stand up for Jesus,
   give courage to the weak,
   be unashamed to praise him,
   be bold his name to speak.
   Confront the cross unflinching,
   Christ's love has set us free;
   he conquered death for ever
   and lives eternally.

206 Such love

Graham Kendrick

Graham Kendrick (b.1950)

1. Such love, pure as the whit - est snow;
such love weeps for the shame I know;
such love, pay - ing the debt I owe;
O Je - sus, such love.

2. Such love, stilling my restlessness;
   such love, filling my emptiness;
   such love, showing me holiness;
   O Jesus, such love.

3. Such love springs from eternity;
   such love, streaming through history;
   such love, fountain of life to me;
   O Jesus, such love.

207 Sun of my soul, thou Saviour dear

John Keble (1792-1866)　　　　　　　　　　　　Herbert Stanley Oakeley (1830-1903)

ABENDS LM

1. Sun of my soul, thou Sa - viour dear, it is not night if thou be near: O may no earth - born cloud a - rise to hide thee from thy ser - vant's eyes.

2. When the soft dews of kindly sleep
   my wearied eyelids gently steep,
   be my last thought, how sweet to rest
   for ever on my Saviour's breast.

3. Abide with me from morn till eve,
   for without thee I cannot live;
   abide with me when night is nigh,
   for without thee I dare not die.

4. Watch by the sick; enrich the poor
   with blessings from thy boundless store;
   be ev'ry mourner's sleep tonight
   like infant's slumbers, pure and light.

208 Take up thy cross, the Saviour said

Charles William Everest (1814-1877)
based on Mark 8, alt.

'As Hymnodus Sacer' (1625)
arr. Felix Mendelssohn (1809-1847)

BRESLAU LM

1. Take up thy cross, the Sa - viour said, if thou wouldst my dis - ci - ple be; de - ny thy - self, the world for - sake, and hum - bly fol - low af - ter me.

2. Take up thy cross – let not its weight
   fill thy weak spirit with alarm:
   his strength shall bear thy spirit up,
   and brace thy heart, and nerve thine arm.

3. Take up thy cross, nor heed the shame,
   nor let thy foolish pride rebel:
   thy Lord for thee the Cross endured,
   to save thy soul from death and hell.

4. Take up thy cross then in his strength,
   and calmly ev'ry danger brave;
   'twill guide thee to a better home,
   and lead to vict'ry o'er the grave.

5. Take up thy cross, and follow Christ,
   nor think till death to lay it down;
   for only those who bear the cross
   may hope to wear the glorious crown.

6. To thee, great Lord, the One in Three,
   all praise for evermore ascend:
   O grant us in our home to see
   the heav'nly life that knows no end.

209 Teach me, my God and King

George Herbert (1593-1633)

Traditional English carol from
William Sandys' 'Christmas Carols' (1833)

SANDYS SM

1. Teach me, my God and King, in all things thee to see; and
what I do in a - ny-thing to do it as for thee.

2. A man that looks on glass,
   on it may stay his eye;
   or, if he pleaseth, through it pass,
   and then the heav'n espy.

3. All may of thee partake;
   nothing can be so mean
   which, with this tincture, 'For thy sake',
   will not grow bright and clean.

4. A servant with this clause
   makes drudgery divine;
   who sweeps a room, as for thy laws,
   makes that and the action fine.

5. This is the famous stone
   that turneth all to gold;
   for that which God doth touch and own
   cannot for less be told.

210 Tell out, my soul

Timothy Dudley-Smith (b.1926)
based on Luke 1:46-55

Walter Greatorex (1877-1949)

WOODLANDS 10 10 10 10

1. Tell out, my soul, the great-ness of the Lord: un-num-bered bles-sings give my spi-rit voice; ten-der to me the pro-mise of his word; in God my Sa-viour shall my heart re-joice.

2. Tell out, my soul, the greatness of his name:
   make known his might, the deeds his arm has done;
   his mercy sure, from age to age the same;
   his holy name, the Lord, the mighty one.

3. Tell out, my soul, the greatness of his might:
   pow'rs and dominions lay their glory by;
   proud hearts and stubborn wills are put to flight,
   the hungry fed, the humble lifted high.

4. Tell out, my soul, the glories of his word:
   firm is his promise, and his mercy sure.
   Tell out, my soul, the greatness of the Lord
   to children's children and for evermore.

211 The angel Gabriel from heaven came

Sabine Baring-Gould (1843-1924)
based on 'Birjina gaztettobat zegoen'

Traditional Basque melody
arr. Richard Lloyd

BIRJINA GAZTETTOBAT ZEGOEN 10 10 12 10

1. The an-gel Ga-bri-el from hea - ven came, his wings as drift-ed snow, his eyes as flame. 'All hail,' said he, 'thou low-ly maid-en, Ma - ry, most high-ly fa-voured la - dy.' Glo - ri - a!

2. 'For known a blessèd Mother thou shalt be.
   All generations laud and honour thee.
   Thy Son shall be Emmanuel, by seers foretold,
   most highly favoured lady.' Gloria!

3. Then gentle Mary meekly bowed her head.
   'To me be as it pleaseth God,' she said.
   'My soul shall laud and magnify his holy name.'
   Most highly favoured lady! Gloria!

4. Of her, Emmanuel, the Christ, was born
   in Bethlehem, all on a Christmas morn;
   and Christian folk throughout the world will ever say:
   'Most highly favoured lady.' Gloria!

212 The Church's one foundation

Samuel John Stone (1839-1900)

AURELIA 76 76 D

1. The Church's one foundation is Jesus Christ, her Lord; she is his new creation, by water and the word; from heav'n he came and sought her to be his holy bride, with his own blood he bought her, and for her life he died.

2. Elect from ev'ry nation, yet one o'er all the earth,
   her charter of salvation, one Lord, one faith, one birth;
   one holy name she blesses, partakes one holy food,
   and to one hope she presses, with ev'ry grace endued.

3. 'Mid toil and tribulation, and tumult of her war,
   she waits the consummation of peace for evermore;
   till with the vision glorious her longing eyes are blest,
   and the great Church victorious shall be the Church at rest.

4. Yet she on earth hath union with God the Three in One,
   and mystic sweet communion with those whose rest is won:
   O happy ones and holy! Lord, give us grace that we
   like them, the meek and lowly, on high may dwell with thee.

213 The day of resurrection

St John of Damascus (c.750)
trans. John Mason Neale (1818-1866)

'Württemburg Gesangbuch' (1784)

ELLACOMBE 76 76 D

1. The day of re-sur-rec - tion! Earth, tell it out a-broad; the pass-o-ver of glad - ness, the pass-o-ver of God! From death to life e-ter - nal, from earth un-to the sky, our Christ hath brought us o - ver with hymns of vic-to - ry.

2. Our hearts be pure from evil, that we may see aright
   the Lord in rays eternal of resurrection-light;
   and list'ning to his accents, may hear so calm and plain
   his own 'All hail' and, hearing, may raise the victor strain.

3. Now let the heav'ns be joyful, and earth her song begin,
   the round world keep high triumph, and all that is therein;
   let all things, seen and unseen, their notes of gladness blend,
   for Christ the Lord hath risen, our joy that hath no end.

214 The day thou gavest, Lord, is ended

John Ellerton (1826-1893) Clement Cotterill Scholefield (1839-1904)

ST CLEMENT 98 98

1. The day thou gav - est, Lord, is end - ed: the dark - ness falls at thy be - hest; to thee our morn - ing hymns a - scend - ed; thy praise shall san - cti - fy our rest.

2. We thank thee that thy Church unsleeping,
   while earth rolls onward into light,
   through all the world her watch is keeping,
   and rests not now by day or night.

3. As o'er each continent and island
   the dawn leads on another day,
   the voice of prayer is never silent,
   nor dies the strain of praise away.

4. The sun that bids us rest is waking
   our brethren 'neath the western sky,
   and hour by hour fresh lips are making
   thy wondrous doings heard on high.

5. So be it, Lord; thy throne shall never,
   like earth's proud empires, pass away;
   thy kingdom stands, and grows for ever,
   till all thy creatures own thy sway.

215 The first Nowell

From William Sandys'
'Christmas Carols, Ancient and Modern' (1833) alt.

Traditional English melody
arr. John Stainer

THE FIRST NOWELL Irregular

1. The first No - well the an - gel did say was to cer - tain poor

shep-herds in fields as they lay: in fields where they lay

keep-ing their sheep, on a cold win-ter's night that was so deep.

Refrain

No - well, No - well, No - well, No - well,

born is the King of Is - ra - el!

2. They lookèd up and saw a star,
   shining in the east, beyond them far,
   and to the earth it gave great light,
   and so it continued both day and night.

3. And by the light of that same star,
   three wise men came from country far;
   to seek for a king was their intent,
   and to follow the star wherever it went.

4. This star drew nigh to the north-west,
   o'er Bethlehem it took its rest,
   and there it did both stop and stay
   right over the place where Jesus lay.

5. Then entered in those wise men three,
   full rev'rently upon their knee,
   and offered there in his presence,
   their gold and myrrh and frankincense.

6. Then let us all with one accord
   sing praises to our heav'nly Lord,
   who with the Father we adore
   and Spirit blest for evermore.

216 The head that once was crowned with thorns

Thomas Kelly (1769-1855)

Jeremiah Clarke (1670-1707)

ST MAGNUS CM

1. The head that once was crowned with thorns is
crowned with glo - ry now: a roy - al di - a -
dem a - dorns the migh - ty vic - tor's brow.

2. The highest place that heav'n affords
   is his, is his by right.
   The King of kings and Lord of lords,
   and heav'n's eternal light.

3. The joy of all who dwell above,
   the joy of all below,
   to whom he manifests his love,
   and grants his name to know.

4. To them the cross, with all its shame,
   with all its grace is giv'n;
   their name an everlasting name,
   their joy the joy of heav'n.

5. They suffer with their Lord below,
   they reign with him above,
   their profit and their joy to know
   the myst'ry of his love.

6. The cross he bore is life and health,
   though shame and death to him;
   his people's hope, his people's wealth,
   their everlasting theme.

217 The King of love my shepherd is

Henry Williams Baker (1821-1877)
based on Psalm 23

John Bacchus Dykes (1823-1876)

DOMINUS REGIT ME 87 87

1. The King of love my shep - herd is, whose

good - ness fail - eth ne - ver; I no - thing lack if

I am his and he is mine for e - ver.

2. Where streams of living water flow
   my ransomed soul he leadeth,
   and where the verdant pastures grow
   with food celestial feedeth.

3. Perverse and foolish oft I strayed,
   but yet in love he sought me,
   and on his shoulder gently laid,
   and home, rejoicing, brought me.

4. In death's dark vale I fear no ill
   with thee, dear Lord, beside me;
   thy rod and staff my comfort still,
   thy cross before to guide me.

5. Thou spread'st a table in my sight,
   thy unction grace bestoweth:
   and O what transport of delight
   from thy pure chalice floweth!

6. And so through all the length of days
   thy goodness faileth never;
   good Shepherd, may I sing thy praise
   within thy house for ever.

218 The Lord's my shepherd

Psalm 23 from 'The Scottish Psalter' (1650)

Melody by Jessie Seymour Irvine (1836-1887)

CRIMOND CM

1. The Lord's my shep - herd, I'll not want. He

makes me down to lie in pas - tures green. He

lead - eth me the qui - et wa - ters by.

2. My soul he doth restore again,
   and me to walk doth make
   within the paths of righteousness,
   e'en for his own name's sake.

3. Yea, though I walk in death's dark vale,
   yet will I fear no ill.
   For thou art with me, and thy rod
   and staff me comfort still.

4. My table thou hast furnishèd
   in presence of my foes,
   my head thou dost with oil anoint,
   and my cup overflows.

5. Goodness and mercy all my life
   shall surely follow me.
   And in God's house for evermore
   my dwelling-place shall be.

219 There is a green hill far away

Cecil Frances Alexander (1818-1895) alt.

William Horsley (1774-1858)

HORSLEY CM

1. There is a green hill far a-way, out-side a ci-ty wall, where

the dear Lord was cru-ci-fied who died to save us all.

2. We may not know, we cannot tell
   what pains he had to bear,
   but we believe it was for us
   he hung and suffered there.

3. He died that we might be forgiv'n,
   he died to make us good;
   that we might go at last to heav'n,
   saved by his precious blood.

4. There was no other good enough
   to pay the price of sin;
   he only could unlock the gate
   of heav'n, and let us in.

5. O, dearly, dearly has he loved,
   and we must love him too,
   and trust in his redeeming blood,
   and try his works to do.

220 There is a Redeemer

Melody Green
based on Scripture

Melody Green
arr. Christopher Tambling

1. There is a Re-dee-mer, Je-sus, God's own Son,
pre-cious Lamb of God, Mes-si-ah, Ho - ly One.

Refrain

Thank you, O my Fa - ther, for giv-ing us your Son, and
leav - ing your Spi-rit till the work on earth is done. done.

2. Jesus, my Redeemer,
   name above all names,
   precious Lamb of God, Messiah,
   O for sinners slain.

3. When I stand in glory,
   I will see his face,
   and there I'll serve my King for ever,
   in that holy place.

221 The Spirit lives to set us free

Walk in the light

Damian Lundy (1944-1997)

Unknown
arr. Christopher Tambling

2. Jesus promised life to all,
   walk, walk in the light.
   The dead were wakened by his call,
   walk, walk in the light.

3. He died in pain on Calvary,
   walk, walk in the light,
   to save the lost like you and me,
   walk, walk in the light.

4. We know his death was not the end,
   walk, walk in the light.
   He gave his Spirit to be our friend,
   walk, walk in the light.

5. By Jesus' love our wounds are healed,
   walk, walk in the light.
   The Father's kindness is revealed,
   walk, walk in the light.

6. The Spirit lives in you and me,
   walk, walk in the light.
   His light will shine for all to see,
   walk, walk in the light.

222 The strife is o'er, the battle done

Latin hymn (17th century)
trans. Francis Pott (1832-1909)

Melody from Melchior Vulpius'
'Gesangbuch' (1609)

GELOB'T SEI GOTT (VULPIUS) 888 and Alleluias

1. The strife is o'er, the bat - tle done; now is the Vic - tor's tri - umph won; O let the song of praise be sung: Al - le - lu - ia, al - le - lu - ia, al - le - lu - ia.

2. Death's mightiest pow'rs have done their worst,
   and Jesus hath his foes dispersed;
   let shouts of praise and joy outburst:
   Alleluia, alleluia, alleluia.

3. On the third morn he rose again
   glorious in majesty to reign;
   O let us swell the joyful strain:
   Alleluia, alleluia, alleluia.

4. Lord, by the stripes which wounded thee
   from death's dread sting thy servants free,
   that we may live, and sing to thee:
   Alleluia, alleluia, alleluia.

223 Thine be the glory

À toi la gloire' by Edmond Louis Budry (1854-1932)
trans. Richard Birch Hoyle (1875-1939)

George Frideric Handel (1685-1759)

MACCABAEUS 10 11 11 11 and Refrain

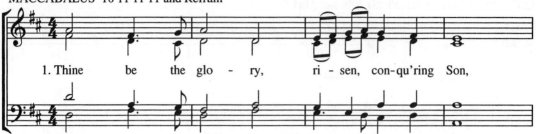

1. Thine be the glo - ry, ri - sen, con - qu'ring Son,

end - less is the vic - t'ry thou o'er death hast won;

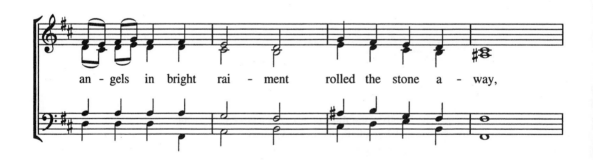

an - gels in bright rai - ment rolled the stone a - way,

kept the fold - ed grave - clothes where thy bo - dy lay.

Refrain
Unison

Thine be the glo - ry, ri - sen, con-qu'ring Son,

end - less is the vic - t'ry thou o'er death hast won.

2. Lo! Jesus meets us, risen from the tomb;
   lovingly he greets us, scatters fear and gloom.
   Let the Church with gladness hymns of triumph sing,
   for her Lord now liveth; death hath lost its sting.

3. No more we doubt thee, glorious Prince of Life!
   Life is naught without thee: aid us in our strife.
   Make us more than conqu'rors through thy deathless love.
   Bring us safe through Jordan to thy home above.

224 Thine for ever! God of love

Mary Fawler Maude (1819-1913) alt.   William Dalrymple Maclagan (1826-1910)

NEWINGTON 77 77

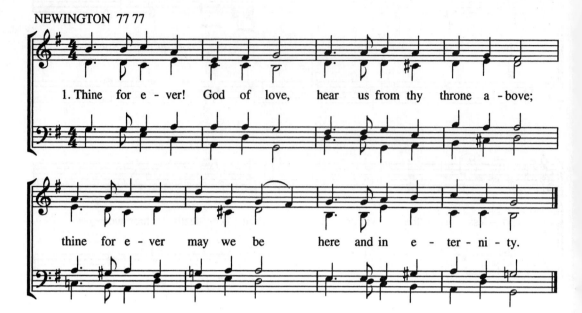

1. Thine for e - ver! God of love, hear us from thy throne a - bove; thine for e - ver may we be here and in e - ter - ni - ty.

2. Thine for ever! Lord of life,
   shield us through our earthly strife;
   thou the life, the truth, the way,
   guide us to the realms of day.

3. Thine for ever! O how blest
   they who find in thee their rest!
   Saviour, guardian, heav'nly friend,
   O defend us to the end.

4. Thine for ever! Shepherd, keep
   us thy frail and trembling sheep;
   safe within thy tender care,
   let us all thy goodness share.

5. Thine for ever! thou our guide,
   all our wants by thee supplied,
   all our sins by thee forgiv'n,
   lead us, Lord, from earth to heav'n.

225 This is the day

Les Garrett

Les Garrett (b.1944)
arr. Christopher Tambling

Unison

1. This is the day, this is the day that the Lord has made, that the Lord has made;
we will re-joice, we will re-joice and be glad in it, and be glad in it.
This is the day that the Lord has made; we will re-joice and be glad in it.
This is the day, this is the day that the Lord has made.

2. This is the day, this is the day
when he rose again, when he rose again;
we will rejoice, we will rejoice
and be glad in it, and be glad in it.
This is the day when he rose again;
we will rejoice and be glad in it.
This is the day, this is the day
when he rose again.

3. This is the day, this is the day
when the Spirit came, when the Spirit came;
we will rejoice, we will rejoice
and be glad in it, and be glad in it.
This is the day when the Spirit came;
we will rejoice and be glad in it.
This is the day, this is the day
when the Spirit came.

226 This joyful Eastertide

George Ratcliffe Woodward (1848-1934)

Traditional Dutch melody
arr. Charles Wood (1866-1926)

THIS JOYFUL EASTERTIDE (VREUCHTEN) 67 67 and Refrain

now hath Christ a - ri - sen, a - ri - sen, a -
ri - sen, a - ri - - sen.

2. My flesh in hope shall rest,
   and for a season slumber;
   till trump from east to west
   shall wake the dead in number.

3. Death's flood hath lost its chill,
   since Jesus crossed the river:
   lover of souls, from ill
   my passing soul deliver.

227 Thou didst leave thy throne

Emily Elizabeth Steele Elliot (1836-1897)
based on Luke 2:7,
adapted by Michael Forster (b.1946)

Timothy Richard Matthews (1826-1910)

MARGARET 10 8 11 8 and Refrain

1. Thou didst leave thy throne and thy king - ly crown when thou

cam - est to earth for me, but in Beth - le- hem's home was there

found no room for thy ho - ly na - ti - vi - ty. *Refrain* O

come to my heart, Lord Je - sus, there is room in my heart for thee.

2. Heaven's arches rang when the angels sang
   and proclaimed thee of royal degree,
   but in lowliest birth didst thou come to earth
   and in deepest humility.

3. Though the fox found rest, and the bird its nest
   in the shade of the cedar tree,
   yet the world found no bed for the Saviour's head
   in the desert of Galilee.

4. Though thou cam'st, Lord, with the living word
   that should set all thy people free,
   yet with treachery, scorn and a crown of thorn
   did they bear thee to Calvary.

5. When the heav'ns shall ring and the angels sing
   at thy coming to victory,
   let thy voice call me home, saying, 'Heav'n has room,
   there is room at my side for thee.'

228 Thou, whose almighty word

John Marriott (1780-1825) alt.

Melody from Madan's 'Collection' (1769)
adapted by Felice de Giardini (1716-1796)

MOSCOW 664 6664

1. Thou, whose al-migh-ty word cha-os and dark-ness heard, and took their flight; hear us, we hum-bly pray, and where the gos-pel day sheds not its glo-rious ray, let there be light.

2. Thou, who didst come to bring
on thy redeeming wing,
healing and sight,
health to the sick in mind,
sight to the inly blind,
O now to humankind
let there be light.

3. Spirit of truth and love,
life-giving, holy Dove,
speed forth thy flight;
move on the water's face,
bearing the lamp of grace,
and in earth's darkest place
let there be light.

4. Holy and blessèd Three,
glorious Trinity,
Wisdom, Love, Might;
boundless as ocean's tide
rolling in fullest pride,
through the earth far and wide
let there be light.

229 Through all the changing scenes of life

Psalm 34 in 'New Version'
(Tate and Brady, 1696)

George Thomas Smart (1776-1867)

WILTSHIRE CM

1. Through all the chang - ing scenes of life, in
trou - ble and in joy, the prai - ses of my
God shall still my heart and tongue em - ploy.

2. O magnify the Lord with me,
   with me exalt his name;
   when in distress to him I called,
   he to my rescue came.

3. The hosts of God encamp around
   the dwellings of the just;
   deliv'rance he affords to all
   who on his succour trust.

4. O make but trial of his love:
   experience will decide
   how blest are they, and only they,
   who in his truth confide.

5. Fear him, ye saints, and you will then
   have nothing else to fear;
   make you his service your delight,
   your wants shall be his care.

6. To Father, Son and Holy Ghost,
   the God whom we adore,
   be glory as it was, is now,
   and shall be evermore.

230 Through the night of doubt and sorrow

Bernhardt Severin Ingemann (1789-1862)
trans. Sabine Baring-Gould (1834-1924) alt.

Martin Shaw (1875-1958)

MARCHING 87 87

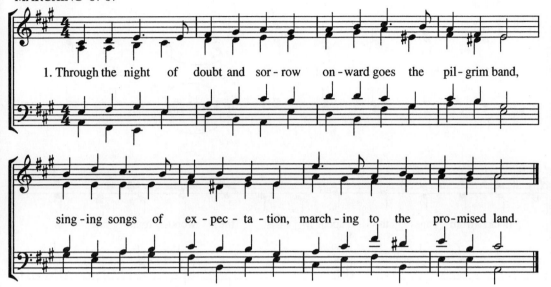

1. Through the night of doubt and sor-row on-ward goes the pil-grim band, sing-ing songs of ex-pec-ta-tion, march-ing to the pro-mised land.

2. Clear before us, through the darkness,
gleams and burns the guiding light;
so we march in hope united,
stepping fearless through the night.

3. One the light of God's own presence
o'er his ransomed people shed,
chasing far the gloom and terror,
bright'ning all the path we tread.

4. One the object of our journey,
one the faith which never tires,
one the earnest looking forward,
one the hope our God inspires.

5. One the strain that lips of thousands
lift as from the heart of one:
one the conflict, one the peril,
one the march in God begun.

6. One the gladness of rejoicing
on the far eternal shore,
where the one almighty Father
reigns in love for evermore.

7. Onward, therefore, fellow pilgrims,
onward with the Cross our aid;
bear its shame and fight its battle,
till we rest beneath its shade.

8. Soon shall come the great awaking,
soon the rending of the tomb;
then the scatt'ring of all shadows,
and the end of toil and gloom.

231 Thy hand, O God, has guided

Edward Hayes Plumptre (1821-1891) alt.

Basil Harwood (1859-1949)

THORNBURY 76 76 D

1. Thy hand, O God, has guid - ed thy flock, from age to age; the wond - rous tale is writ - ten, full clear, on ev - 'ry page; our fore - bears owned thy good - ness, and we their deeds re - cord; and both of this bear wit - ness: one

Church, one Faith, one Lord.

2. Thy heralds brought glad tidings
   to greatest, as to least;
   they bade them rise, and hasten
   to share the great King's feast;
   and this was all their teaching,
   in ev'ry deed and word,
   to all alike proclaiming:
   one Church, one Faith, one Lord.

3. Through many a day of darkness,
   through many a scene of strife,
   the faithful few fought bravely
   to guard the nation's life.
   Their gospel of redemption,
   sin pardoned, hope restored,
   was all in this enfolded:
   one Church, one Faith, one Lord.

4. And we, shall we be faithless?
   Shall hearts fail, hands hang down?
   Shall we evade the conflict,
   and cast away our crown?
   Not so: in God's deep counsels
   some better thing is stored:
   we will maintain, unflinching,
   one Church, one Faith, one Lord.

5. Thy mercy will not fail us,
   nor leave thy work undone;
   with thy right hand to help us,
   the vict'ry shall be won;
   and then by all creation,
   thy name shall be adored.
   And this shall be their anthem:
   One Church, one Faith, one Lord.

232 Thy kingdom come, O God

Lewis Hensley (1824-1905) alt.

Leighton George Hayne (1836-1883)

ST CECILIA 66 66

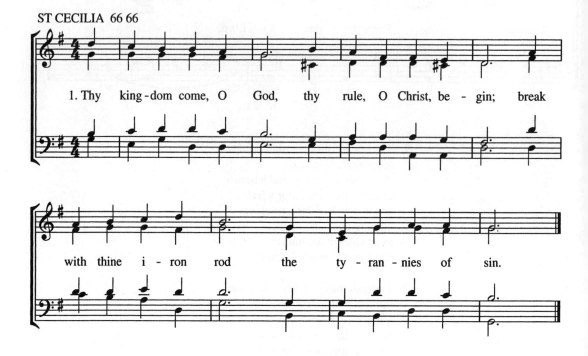

1. Thy king-dom come, O God, thy rule, O Christ, be - gin; break
with thine i - ron rod the ty - ran - nies of sin.

2. Where is thy reign of peace
   and purity and love?
   When shall all hatred cease,
   as in the realms above?

3. When comes the promised time
   when war shall be no more,
   and lust, oppression, crime
   shall flee thy face before?

4. We pray thee, Lord, arise,
   and come in thy great might;
   revive our longing eyes,
   which languish for thy sight.

5. Some scorn thy sacred name,
   and wolves devour thy fold;
   by many deeds of shame
   we learn that love grows cold.

6. O'er lands both near and far
   thick darkness broodeth yet:
   arise, O morning star,
   arise, and never set.

233 To be in your presence

My desire

Noel Richards

Noel Richards

2. To rest in your presence,
   not rushing away,
   to cherish each moment,
   here I would stay.

234 To God be the glory!

Frances Jane van Alstyne (Fanny J. Crosby) (1820-1915)   William Howard Doane (1832-1916)

TO GOD BE THE GLORY 11 11 11 11 and Refrain

1. To God be the glo - ry! great things he hath done; so loved he the
world that he gave us his Son; who yield - ed his life an a -
tone - ment for sin, and o - pened the life - gate that all may go in.

Refrain

Praise the Lord, praise the Lord! let the earth hear his voice; praise the
Lord, praise the Lord! let the peo - ple re - joice: O

come to the Fa - ther, through Je - sus the Son, and

give him the glo - ry; great things he hath done!

2. O perfect redemption, the purchase of blood!
   to ev'ry believer the promise of God;
   the vilest offender who truly believes,
   that moment from Jesus a pardon receives.

3. Great things he hath taught us, great things he hath done,
   and great our rejoicing through Jesus the Son;
   but purer, and higher, and greater will be
   our wonder, our rapture, when Jesus we see.

235 To thee, O Lord, our hearts we raise

William Chatterton Dix (1837-1898) alt.

Arthur Seymour Sullivan (1842-1900)

GOLDEN SHEAVES 87 87 D

1. To thee, O Lord, our hearts we raise in hymns of a - do - ra - tion; to

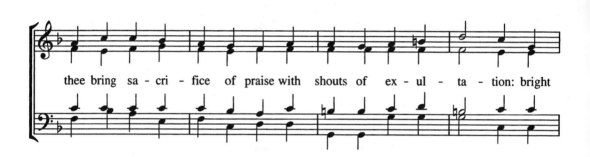

thee bring sa - cri - fice of praise with shouts of ex - ul - ta - tion: bright

robes of gold the fields a - dorn, the hills with joy are ring - ing, the

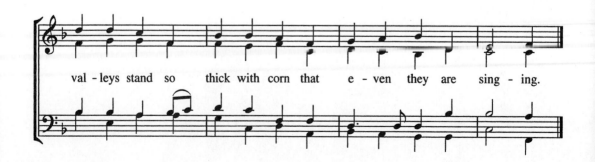

val - leys stand so thick with corn that e - ven they are sing - ing.

2. And now, on this our festal day,
   thy bounteous hand confessing,
   upon thine altar, Lord, we lay
   the first-fruits of thy blessing:
   by thee our souls are truly fed
   with gifts of grace supernal;
   thou who dost give us earthly bread,
   give us the bread eternal.

3. We bear the burden of the day,
   and often toil seems dreary;
   but labour ends with sunset ray,
   and rest comes for the weary:
   may we, the angel-reaping o'er,
   stand at the last accepted,
   Christ's golden sheaves for evermore
   to garners bright elected.

4. O blessèd is that land of God,
   where saints abide for ever;
   where golden fields spread far and broad,
   where flows the crystal river:
   the strains of all its holy throng
   with ours today are blending;
   thrice blessèd is that harvest-song
   which never hath an ending.

236 To the name of our salvation

'Gloriosi Salvatoris' (15th century)
trans. John Mason Neale (1818-1866) alt.

Caspar Ett's
'Cantica Sacra' (1840)

ORIEL 87 87 87

1. To the name of our sal-va-tion laud and hon-our let us pay,
which for ma-ny a ge-ne-ra-tion hid in God's fore-know-ledge lay,
but with ho-ly ex-ul-ta-tion we may sing a-loud to-day.

2. Jesus is the name we treasure,
name beyond what words can tell;
name of gladness, name of pleasure,
ear and heart delighting well;
name of sweetness passing measure,
saving us from sin and hell.

3. 'Tis the name for adoration,
name for songs of victory;
name for holy meditation
in the vale of misery;
name for joyful veneration
by the citizens on high.

4. 'Tis the name that whoso preacheth
speaks like music to the ear;
who in prayer his name beseecheth
sweetest comfort findeth near;
who its perfect wisdom reacheth
heav'nly joy possesseth here.

5. Jesus is the name exalted
over ev'ry other name;
in this name, whene'er assaulted,
we can put our foes to shame:
strength to them who else had halted,
eyes to blind, and feet to lame.

6. Therefore we in love adoring
this most blessèd name revere,
holy Jesus, thee imploring
so to write it in us here,
that hereafter, heav'nward soaring,
we may sing with angels there.

237 Unto us a boy is born

'Puer nobis nascitur' (15th century)
trans. Percy Dearmer (1867-1936) alt.

From 'Piae Cantiones' (1582)
arr. Adrian Vernon Fish

PUER NOBIS 76 77

1. Un - to us a boy is born! King of all cre - a - tion; came he to a world for - lorn, the Lord of ev - 'ry na - tion, the Lord of ev - 'ry na - tion.

2. Cradled in a stall was he,
   watched by cows and asses;
   but the very beasts could see
   that he the world surpasses,
   that he the world surpasses.

3. Then the fearful Herod cried,
   'Pow'r is mine in Jewry!'
   So the blameless children died
   the victims of his fury,
   the victims of his fury.

4. Now may Mary's Son, who came
   long ago to love us,
   lead us all with hearts aflame
   unto the joys above us,
   unto the joys above us.

5. Omega and Alpha he!
   Let the organ thunder,
   while the choir with peals of glee
   shall rend the air asunder,
   shall rend the air asunder.

238 We are marching

Traditional South African;
v.1 trans. Anders Nyberg;
vs. 2 & 3 trans. Andrew Maries

Traditional South African
arr. Anders Nyberg

SIYAHAMBA 99 99 59 59

1. We are march - ing in the light of God, we are march-ing in the light of God. We are march - ing in the light of God, We are march-ing in the light of God, We are march-ing in the light of, the light of God. We are march-ing, march-ing, we are

Oo - ooh! We are march-ing in the light of God.

march-ing, march-ing, we are march-ing in the light of, the

march-ing, march-ing, we are march-ing in the light of God.

We are march-ing,

light of God. We are march-ing, march-ing, we are

Oo-ooh! We are march-ing in the light of God.

march-ing, march-ing, we are march-ing in the light of God.

2. We are living in the love of God . . .

3. We are moving in the pow'r of God . . .

239 We have a gospel to proclaim

Edward Joseph Burns (b.1938)

From William Gardiner's
'Sacred Melodies' (1815)

FULDA LM

1. We have a gos - pel to pro - claim, good news for all through - out the earth; the gos - pel of a Sa - viour's name: we sing his glo - ry, tell his worth.

2. Tell of his birth at Bethlehem,
   not in a royal house or hall,
   but in a stable dark and dim,
   the Word made flesh, a light for all.

3. Tell of his death at Calvary,
   hated by those he came to save;
   in lonely suff'ring on the cross:
   for all he loved, his life he gave.

4. Tell of that glorious Easter morn,
   empty the tomb, for he was free;
   he broke the pow'r of death and hell
   that we might share his victory.

5. Tell of his reign at God's right hand,
   by all creation glorified.
   He sends his Spirit on his Church
   to live for him, the Lamb who died.

6. Now we rejoice to name him King:
   Jesus is Lord of all the earth.
   This gospel-message we proclaim:
   we sing his glory, tell his worth.

240 We love the place, O God

William Bullock (1798-1874)
and Henry Williams Baker (1821-1877)

Henry Lascelles Jenner (1820-1898)

QUAM DILECTA 66 66

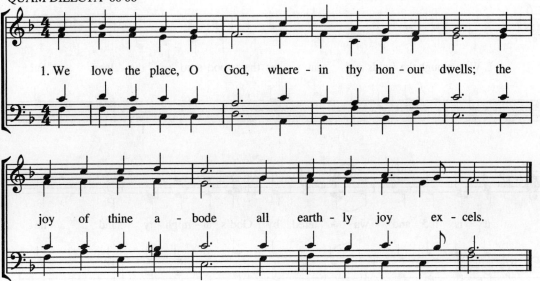

1. We love the place, O God, where - in thy hon - our dwells; the
joy of thine a - bode all earth - ly joy ex - cels.

2. It is the house of prayer,
wherein thy servants meet;
and thou, O Lord, art there
thy chosen flock to greet.

3. We love the sacred font;
for there the holy Dove
to pour is ever wont
his blessing from above.

4. We love thine altar, Lord;
O what on earth so dear?
For there, in faith adored,
we find thy presence near.

5. We love the word of life,
the word that tells of peace,
of comfort in the strife,
and joys that never cease.

6. We love to sing below
for mercies freely giv'n;
but O, we long to know
the triumph-song of heav'n.

7. Lord Jesus, give us grace
on earth to love thee more,
in heav'n to see thy face,
and with thy saints adore.

241 We plough the fields and scatter

Matthias Claudius (1740-1815)
trans. Jane Montgomery Campbell (1817-1878) alt.

Johann Abraham Peter Schulz (1747-1800)
harm. John Bacchus Dykes (1832-1876)

WIR PFLÜGEN 76 76 D and Refrain

1. We plough the fields and scat - ter the good seed on the land, but

it is fed and wa - tered by God's al - migh - ty hand: he

sends the snow in win - ter, the warmth to swell the grain, the

breez - es and the sun - shine, and soft, re - fresh - ing rain.

Refrain

All good gifts a - round us are sent from heav'n a - bove; then

thank the Lord, O thank the Lord, for all his love.

2. He only is the maker
   of all things near and far;
   he paints the wayside flower,
   he lights the evening star;
   he fills the earth with beauty,
   by him the birds are fed;
   much more to us, his children,
   he gives our daily bread.

3. We thank thee then, O Father,
   for all things bright and good:
   the seed-time and the harvest,
   our life, our health, our food.
   Accept the gifts we offer
   for all thy love imparts,
   and, what thou most desirest,
   our humble, thankful hearts.

242 We three kings of Orient are

John Henry Hopkins alt.

John Henry Hopkins (1820-1891)

KINGS OF ORIENT 88 86 and Refrain

1. We three kings of O - ri - ent are; bear - ing
gifts we tra - verse a - far; field and foun - tain,
moor and moun - tain, fol - low - ing yon - der star.

Refrain

O star of won - der, star of night,
star with roy - al beau - ty bright, west - ward lead - ing,

still pro - ceed - ing, guide us to thy per - fect light.

2. Born a King on Bethlehem plain,
   gold I bring, to crown him again,
   King for ever, ceasing never,
   over us all to reign.

3. Frankincense to offer have I,
   incense owns a Deity nigh,
   prayer and praising, gladly raising,
   worship him, God most high.

4. Myrrh is mine, its bitter perfume
   breathes a life of gathering gloom;
   sorrowing, sighing, bleeding, dying,
   sealed in the stone-cold tomb.

5. Glorious now behold him arise,
   King and God and sacrifice;
   alleluia, alleluia,
   earth to heav'n replies.

243 What a friend we have in Jesus

Joseph Medlicott Scriven (1819-1886)

Charles Crozat Converse (1832-1918)

WHAT A FRIEND (CONVERSE) 87 87 D

1. What a friend we have in Je - sus, all our sins and griefs to bear!
What a pri - vi - lege to car - ry ev - 'ry-thing to him in prayer!
O what peace we of-ten for - feit, O what need-less pain we bear,
all be-cause we do not car - ry ev - 'ry- thing to God in prayer!

2. Have we trials and temptations?
   Is there trouble anywhere?
   We should never be discouraged:
   take it to the Lord in prayer!
   Can we find a friend so faithful,
   who will all our sorrows share?
   Jesus knows our ev'ry weakness –
   take it to the Lord in prayer!

3. Are we weak and heavy-laden,
   cumbered with a load of care?
   Jesus only is our refuge,
   take it to the Lord in prayer!
   Do thy friends despise, forsake thee?
   Take it to the Lord in prayer!
   In his arms he'll take and shield thee,
   thou wilt find a solace there.

244 When all thy mercies, O my God

Joseph Addison (1672-1719) alt.

Frederick Arthur Gore Ouseley (1825-1889)

CONTEMPLATION CM

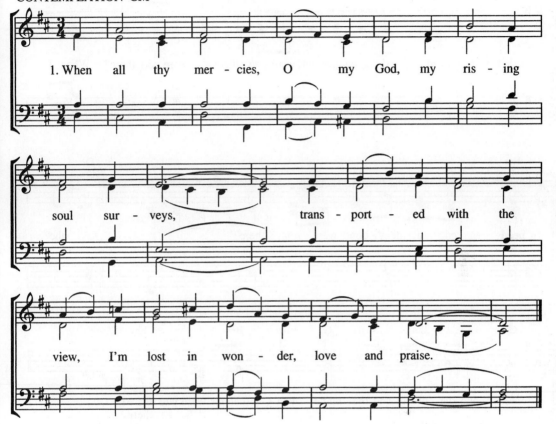

1. When all thy mer - cies, O my God, my ris - ing soul sur - veys, trans - port - ed with the view, I'm lost in won - der, love and praise.

2. Unnumbered comforts to my soul
   thy tender care bestowed,
   before my infant heart conceived
   from whom those comforts flowed.

3. When in such slipp'ry paths I ran
   in childhood's careless days,
   thine arm unseen conveyed me safe,
   to walk in adult ways.

4. When worn with sickness oft hast thou
   with health renewed my face;
   and when in sins and sorrows sunk,
   revived my soul with grace.

5. Ten thousand thousand precious gifts
   my daily thanks employ,
   and not the least a cheerful heart
   which tastes those gifts with joy.

6. Through ev'ry period of my life
   thy goodness I'll pursue,
   and after death in distant worlds
   the glorious theme renew.

7. Through all eternity to thee
   a joyful song I'll raise;
   for O! eternity's too short
   to utter all thy praise.

245 When I needed a neighbour

Sydney Carter

Sydney Carter (b.1915)
arr. Andrew Moore

NEIGHBOUR 13 10 and Refrain

1. When I need-ed a neigh-bour, were you there, were you there? When I need-ed a neigh-bour, were you there? And the creed and the col-our and the name won't mat-ter, were you there? (I'll be there.)

2. I was hungry and thirsty,
were you there, were you there?
I was hungry and thirsty,
were you there?

3. I was cold, I was naked,
were you there, were you there?
I was cold, I was naked,
were you there?

4. When I needed a shelter,
were you there, were you there?
When I needed a shelter,
were you there?

5. When I needed a healer,
were you there, were you there?
When I needed a healer,
were you there?

6. Wherever you travel,
I'll be there, I'll be there,
wherever you travel,
I'll be there.

246 When I survey the wondrous cross

Isaac Watts (1674-1748)

Adapted by Edward Miller (1735-1807)

ROCKINGHAM LM

1. When I survey the wondrous cross on which the Prince of Glory died, my richest gain I count but loss, and pour contempt on all my pride.

2. Forbid it, Lord, that I should boast,
   save in the death of Christ, my God:
   all the vain things that charm me most,
   I sacrifice them to his blood.

3. See from his head, his hands, his feet,
   sorrow and love flow minging down:
   did e'er such love and sorrow meet,
   or thorns compose so rich a crown?

4. Were the whole realm of nature mine,
   that were an off'ring far too small;
   love so amazing, so divine,
   demands my soul, my life, my all.

247 While shepherds watched

Nahum Tate (1652-1715)

From Este's 'Psalter' (1592)

WINCHESTER OLD CM

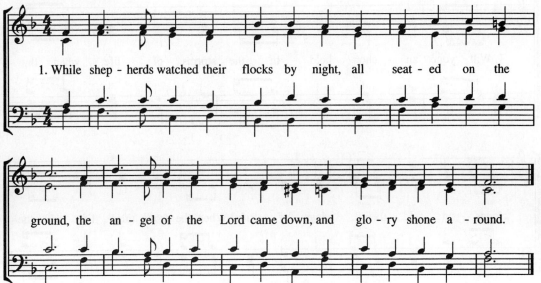

1. While shep - herds watched their flocks by night, all seat - ed on the ground, the an - gel of the Lord came down, and glo - ry shone a - round.

2. 'Fear not,' said he, (for mighty dread
had seized their troubled mind)
'glad tidings of great joy I bring
to you and all mankind.

3. To you in David's town this day
is born of David's line
a Saviour, who is Christ the Lord;
and this shall be the sign:

4. The heav'nly babe you there shall find
to human view displayed,
all meanly wrapped in swathing bands,
and in a manger laid.'

5. Thus spake the seraph, and forthwith
appeared a shining throng
of angels praising God, who thus
addressed their joyful song:

6. 'All glory be to God on high,
and on the earth be peace,
goodwill henceforth from heav'n to all
begin and never cease.'

248 Will your anchor hold

Priscilla Jane Owens (1829-1899)

William James Kirkpatrick (1838-1921)

WILL YOUR ANCHOR HOLD Irregular and Refrain

1. Will your an - chor hold in the storms of life, when the clouds un - fold their wings of strife? When the strong tides lift, and the ca - bles strain, will your an - chor drift, or firm re - main?

Refrain

We have an an - chor that keeps the soul stead - fast and sure while the bil - lows roll; fast-ened to the rock which can - not move, ground-ed firm and deep in the Sa - viour's love!

2. Will your anchor hold in the straits of fear,
   when the breakers roar and the reef is near?
   While the surges rage, and the wild winds blow,
   shall the angry waves then your bark o'erflow?

3. Will your anchor hold in the floods of death,
   when the waters cold chill your latest breath?
   On the rising tide you can never fail,
   while your anchor holds within the veil.

4. Will your eyes behold through the morning light,
   the city of gold and the harbour bright?
   Will you anchor safe by the heav'nly shore,
   when life's storms are past for evermore?

249 Ye choirs of new Jerusalem

'Chorus novæ Jerusalem'
by St Fulbert of Chartres (c.1028)
trans. Robert Campbell (1814-1868)

Henry John Gauntlett (1805-1876)

ST FULBERT CM

1. Ye choirs of new Je - ru - sa -lem, your sweet -est notes em - ploy, the

Pas - chal vic - to - ry to hymn in strains of ho - ly joy.

2. For Judah's Lion burst his chains,
   and crushed the serpent's head;
   and brought with him, from death's domain,
   the long-imprisoned dead.

3. From hell's devouring jaws the prey
   alone our leader bore;
   his ransomed hosts pursue their way
   where he hath gone before.

4. Triumphant in his glory now
   his sceptre ruleth all:
   earth, heav'n and hell before him bow
   and at his footstool fall.

5. While joyful thus his praise we sing,
   his mercy we implore,
   into his palace bright to bring,
   and keep us evermore.

6. All glory to the Father be,
   all glory to the Son,
   all glory, Holy Ghost, to thee,
   while endless ages run.

250 Ye holy angels bright

Richard Baxter (1615-1691)
and John Hampden Gurney (1802-1862)

John Darwall (1731-1789)
harm. William Henry Monk (1823-1889)

DARWALL'S 148TH 66 66 44 44

1. Ye ho-ly an-gels bright, who wait at God's right hand, or through the realms of light fly at your Lord's com - mand, as - sist our song, for else the theme too high doth seem for mor - tal tongue.

2. Ye blessèd souls at rest,
who ran this earthly race,
and now, from sin released,
behold the Saviour's face,
God's praises sound,
as in his sight
with sweet delight
ye do abound.

3. Ye saints, who toil below,
adore your heav'nly King,
and onward as ye go
some joyful anthem sing;
take what he gives
and praise him still,
through good or ill,
who ever lives.

4. My soul, bear thou thy part,
triumph in God above:
and with a well-tuned heart
sing thou the songs of love;
let all thy days
till life shall end,
whate'er he send,
be filled with praise.

251 Ye servants of God

Charles Wesley (1707-1788)

From the 'Paderborn Gesangbuch' (1765)

PADERBORN 10 10 11 11

1. Ye ser-vants of God, your Mas-ter pro-claim, and
pub-lish a-broad his won-der-ful name; the
name all vic-to-rious of Je-sus ex-tol: his
king-dom is glo-rious, and rules o-ver all.

2. God ruleth on high, almighty to save;
   and still he is nigh: his presence we have:
   the great congregation his triumph shall sing,
   ascribing salvation to Jesus our King.

3. Salvation to God who sits on the throne!
   let all cry aloud, and honour the Son.
   The praises of Jesus the angels proclaim,
   fall down on their faces, and worship the Lamb.

4. Then let us adore, and give him his right:
   all glory and pow'r, all wisdom and might,
   and honour and blessing, with angels above,
   and thanks never-ceasing, and infinite love.

252 Ye servants of the Lord

Philip Doddridge (1702-1751) alt.

Melody from Johannes Leisentritt's
'Catholicum Hymnologium Germanicum' (1584)
adapted by William Henry Havergal (1793-1870)

NARENZA SM

1. Ye ser-vants of the Lord, each for his com-ing wait, ob -

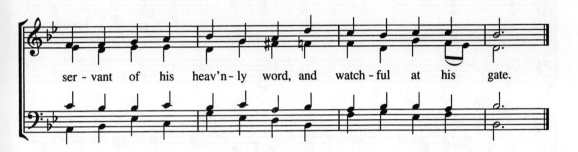

ser - vant of his heav'n-ly word, and watch-ful at his gate.

2. Let all your lamps be bright,
   and trim the golden flame;
   gird up your loins as in his sight,
   for awesome is his name.

3. Watch! 'tis your Lord's command,
   and while we speak, he's near;
   mark the first signal of his hand,
   and ready all appear.

4. O happy servants they,
   in such a posture found,
   who share their Saviour's triumph day,
   with joy and honour crowned.

5. Christ shall the banquet spread
   with his own royal hand,
   and raise each faithful servant's head
   amid th'angelic band.

253 You shall go out with joy

The trees of the field

Steffi Geiser Rubin
and Stuart Dauermann

Steffi Geiser Rubin
and Stuart Dauermann

Indexes

Index of Composers, Arrangers and Sources of Music

Arrangers are shown indented and in italics

Adkins, Donna 71
American traditional 18, 107
Appleford, Patrick 74, 138
As Hymnodus Sacer 208

Bach, Johann Sebastian 28, 41
  Bach, Johann Sebastian 28
Bankhead, Dave 54
Barnard, John 47, 87
Barthélémon, François Hippolyte 30
Basque traditional 211
Baughen, Michael 137
Beaumont, Geoffrey 170
Beethoven, Ludwig van 73
Bennard, George 174
Bilbrough, Dave 1, 105
Bourgeois, Louis 15
Boyce William 56
Brethorst, Leona von 116
Brierley, Michael 29
Brown, Arthur Henry 58

Campbell, Thomas 19
Caniadu y Cyssegr 109
Cantica Sacra 236
Carter, Sydney 107, 178, 245
Catholicum Hymnologium Germanicum 58, 252
Choralbuch, Leipzig 48
Clarke, Jeremiah 110, 216
Coelho, Terrye 70
Converse, Charles Crozat 243
Croatian traditional 81, 189
Croft, William 168, 184
Crüger, Johann 92, 157
Cullen, Tim 93
  Cummings, William Hayman 96

Damon, William 139
Daniels, John 26
Darwall, John 250
Dauermann, Stuart 253
Davies, Henry Walford 82
Doane, William Howard 234
Dunn, Fred 127
Dutch traditional 226
Dykes, John Bacchus 65, 69, 99, 108, 155, 126, 130, 182, 190, 217, 241

Ellor, James 10
Elvey, George Job 59, 60
English traditional 16, 67, 97, 108, 113, 115, 171, 177, 209, 215
Este's Psalter 247
Ett, Casper 236
European Psalmist 56
Evans, David J. 32
Ewing, Alexander 117

Ferguson, William Harold 170
Filitz, Friedrich 131
  Fish, Adrian Vernon 16
Fishel, Donald 5
Flemish traditional 23
French traditional 23, 62, 158
Freylinghausen, Johann Anastasius 179

Gaelic traditional 150
Gardiner, William 239
Garrett, Les 225
Gauntlett, Henry John 124, 166, 175, 249
Geistliche Kirchengesang 4
Genevan Psalter 15
German Traditional 3, 122
Giardini, Felice de 228
Gibbons, Orlando 21
Gillman, Bob 36
Goss, John 188, 198
Greatorex, Walter 210
Green, Melody 220
Grüber, Franz 200

Hammond, Mary Jane 159
  Hand, Colin 35, 62, 70, 79, 140, 150, 161, 178, 200
Handel, George Frideric 194, 223
Harmonischer Liederschatz 38
Harwood, Basil 132, 231
Hassler, Hans Leo 181
Hatton, John 72
Havergal, William Henry 38, 252
Haweis, Thomas 49, 190
  Hawkins, E. 44
Haydn, Franz Joseph 81, 189
Hayford, Jack W. 146
Hayne, Leighton George 145, 232
Helmore, Thomas 161
Hewer, Jenny 68
Himmels-Lust, Jenna 41
  Hine, Stuart K. 172
Hintze, Jacob 28
Holst, Gustav 112, 167
  Holst, Gustav 83
Hopkins, John Henry 242
Horsley, William 219
Howells, Herbert 13
Hughes, John 90
Hundert Arien, Dresden 46
Hymn Tunes of the United Brethren 133

  Iliff, David 137
Ireland, John 154
Irish traditional 35, 106, 140
Irvine, Jessie Seymour 218
Iverson, Daniel 203

Jackson, Robert 40
Jarman, Thomas 164
Jenkins, David 111
Jenner, Henry Lascelles 240
Jones, John David 129

Kendrick, Graham 12, 109, 78, 141, 148, 149, 206
Kirkbride, Mary 42
Kirkpatrick, Willaim James 248
Knapp, Phoebe Palmer 37
Knapp, William 193
Knecht, Justin Heinrich 169
Kocher, Conrad 27, 76

Lahee, Henry 53
Leisentritt, Johannes 58, 252
  Lloyd Richard 18, 23, 31, 211
Lockhart, Charles 40, 204
Lyra Davidica 121

Maclagan, William Dalrymple 39, 224
Madan's Collection 228
Magdalen Hospital Hymns 102
Mansell, David J. 123
Markland, Gerard 64
Mason, Lowell 155
Matthews, Timothy Richard 227
Mayhew, Kevin 186
  Mendelssohn, Felix 208
Miller, Edward 246
  Miller, Edward 151
Monk, Edwin George 24
Monk, William Henry 2, 16, 21, 27, 29, 76, 91, 94, 121, 142, 157, 201, 250
  Monk, William Henry 92
  Moore, Andrew 5, 14, 20, 22, 26, 36, 50, 52, 64, 71, 83, 245
Morgan, Patricia 54
Murray, James R 31
Musikalisches Handbuch 195

Neander, Joachim 57
Nicholson, Sydney Hugo 91, 134
Novello, Vincent 162, 176
Nurnbergisches Gesangbuch 77
  Nyberg, Anders 238
Nystrom, Martin 25

Oakeley, Herbert Stanley 207
Ouseley, Frederick Arthur Gore 244

Paculabo, John 50
Paderborn Gesangbuch 251
Parry, Charles Hubert Hastings 20, 61, 180
Parry, Joseph 118
Peace, Albert Lister 173
Perry, Michael 199
Petrus, Theodoricus 165
Piae Cantiones 83, 88, 165, 237
Playford, John 84
Praetorius, Michael 3
Praxis Pietatis Melica 191
Pritchard, Rowland Huw 7
Proper Sarum Melody 52
Psalmodia Evangelica 125
Psalmody in Miniature 151
Psalms in English Metre, The 139
Purcell, Henry 44
Purday, Charles Henry 130

Ravenscroft, Thomas 63, 95
  Rawsthorne, Noel 106, 107
Redhead, Richard 42, 196
Redman, Matt 120
Reinagle, Alexander Robert 104
Rheinhardt MS Üttingen 185
Richards, Hubert J. 86
Richards, Noel 11, 233
Roberts, John 109
Rowlands, William Penfro 143
Rubin, Steffi Geiser 253
Ryecroft, Keith 50

Sacred Melodies 239
Sandy, William 209
Scholefield, Clement Cotterill 214
Schutte, Dan 114
Scottish Psalter 84, 163
Select Hymns with Tunes Annext 136
Shaw, Geoffrey 76
Shaw, Martin 67, 98, 230

Shrubsole, William 10
Sibelius, Jean 33
Silcher, Friedrich 66
Smart, George Thomas 229
Smart, Henry 44, 85, 128, 135
Smith Jnr., Leonard E. 103
Smith, Henry 80
Smith, Isaac 69
South African traditional 238
Stainer, John 8, 56, 143, 152
  Stainer, John 88, 215
Steggall, Charles 202
  Stent, Keith 12, 86, 103
Sullivan, Arthur Seymour 6, 235
  Sullivan, Arthur Seymour 113
Swedish traditional 172

  Tambling, Christopher 1, 73, 158, 187, 199, 220, 221, 225
Taylor, Cyril Vincent 81
Temple, Sebastian 147
Terry, Richard Runciman 60, 190
Teschner, Melchior 9
Thorne, Edward Henry 119
Thrupp, Joseph Francis 41
Tochter Sion 17
Toplady, Augustus Montague 196
Townend, Stuart 101
Traditional 79
Turner, Roy 14
Tuttle, Carl 100

Vulpius, Melchoir 222

Wade, John Francis 160
Wainwright, John 43
  Warren, Norman 170
Warwickshire traditional 74
Webb, George James 205
Webbe, Samuel 55, 156
Weisse, M. 142
Welsh traditional 109
Werner's, Johann Gottlob 48
Wesley, John 136, 144
Wesley, Samuel Sebastian 45, 56, 183, 192, 212
Wilkes, John Bernard 133
William, Thomas 125
Williams, Aaron 151
Williams, Ralph Vaughan 51, 67, 75, 122
  Williams, Ralph Vaughan 4, 7, 74, 97, 108, 115, 171, 177
Williams, Robert 91
  Wood, Charles 23, 62, 226
Württemberg Gesangbuch 213

Zschech, Darlene 153

Index of Authors and Sources of Text

A toi la gloire 223
Ad regias Agni dapes 28
Adams, Sarah Flower 155
Addison, Joseph 244
Adkins, Donna 71
Alexander, Cecil Frances 16, 119, 175, 219
Alford, Henry 59
Alstyne, Frances Jane van 37, 234
Appleford, Patrick 138
Arnold, J. 121

Baker, Henry Williams 142, 179, 180, 217, 240
Bankhead, Dave 54
Baring-Gould, Sabine 211, 230
Baxter, Richard 250
Bennard, George 174
Bilbrough, Dave 1, 105
Birgina gaztettobat zegoen 211
Bishop Synesius 139
Blake, William 20
Bode, John E. 170
Bonar, Horatius 108
Book of Hours 82
Borthwick, Jane L. 33
Brethorst, Leona von 116
Bridges, Matthew 60
Bridges, Robert 181
Bright, William 21, 176
Brooks, Philips 171
Budry, Edmond Louis 223
Bullock, William 240
Bunyan, John 97
Burns, Edward Joseph 239
Byrne, Mary 35
Byrom, John 43

Campbell, Jane Montgomery 241
Campbell, Robert 28, 249
Carter, Sydney 107, 178, 245
Caswall, Edward 17, 55, 94, 126, 152, 198
Cennick, John 136
Chandler, John 45
Chatfield, Allen William 139
Chisholm, Thomas Obadiah 89
Chorus novae Jerusalem 249
Christmas Carols, Ancient and Modern 215
Clairvaux, St Bernard of 126
Claudius, Matthias 241
Coelho, Terrye 70
Compleat Psalmodist 121
Conder, Josiah 39
Cooper, Edward 69
Corde natus ex parentis 165
Cosin, John 52
Cotterill, Thomas 91
Cowper, William 84, 163
Cox, Frances Elizabeth 124
Crosby, Fanny J. 37, 234
Crossman, Samuel 154
Crum, John Macleod Campbell 158
Cullen, Tim 93

Dale, Alan 86
Damascus, St John of 58
Daniels, John 26

Dauermann, Stuart 253
Day's Psalter 15
De Contemptu Mundi 117
Dearmer, Percy 83, 97, 122, 237
Discendi, amor santo 51
Dix, William Chatterton 7, 27, 235
Doddridge, Philip 95, 151, 252
Draper, William Henry 4
Dudley-Smith, Timothy 73, 137, 210
Dunn, Fred 127

Edmeston, James 131
Ellerton, John 182, 197, 214
Elliott, Charlotte 128
Elliott, Emily Elizabeth Steele 227
English traditional 177
Evans, David J. 32
Everest, Charles William 208

Farjeon, Eleanor 150
Fishel, Donald 5
Forster, Michael 10, 52, 77, 151, 227
Foundling Hospital Collection 189
Fullerton, William Young 106

Garrett, Les 225
Gellert, Christian Fürchtegott 124
Gerhardt, Paul 181
Gilman, Bob 36
Gloria, laus et honor 9
Gloriosi Salvatoris 236
Grant, Robert 184
Great O Antiphons 161
Green, Melody 220
Gurney, John Hampden 250

Hall, William John 38
Hardy, Henry Earnest 162
Hatch, Edwin 40
Hayford, Jack W. 146
Head, Elizabeth Ann Porter 159
Heber, Reginald 41, 99
Hensley, Lewis 232
Herbert, George 129, 132, 209
Hewer, Jenny 68
Hine, Stuart K. 172
Holloway, Jean 205
Hopkins, John Henry 242
Hort, Fenton John Anthony 182
How, William Walsham 75, 115
Hoyle, Richard Birch 223
Hull, Eleanor 35
Hupton, Job 57

Ingemann, Bernhardt, Severin 230
Iverson, Daniel 203

Johnson, Samuel 49

Keble, John 38, 156, 207
Keen, Richard 102
Kelly, Thomas 216
Kempis, Thomas à 135
Ken, Thomas 30
Kendrick, Graham 12, 78, 141, 148, 149, 206
Kethe, William 15

Kirkpatrick, William James 31
Kitchin, George William 134

Langton, Stephen 55
Leeson, Jane Elizabeth 145
Littledale, Richard F. 51
Lundy, Damian 221
Lyte, Henry Francis 2, 85, 188

Madan, Martin 96, 136
Mansell, David J. 123
Mant, Richard 42
Maries, Andrew 238
Markland, Gerard 64
Marriott, John 228
Matheson, George 173
Maude, Mary Fawler 224
Maurus, Rabanus 52
Mayhew, Kevin 186
McClellan, Sue 50
Meine Hoffnung stehet feste 13
Milman, Henry Hart 195
Milton, John 133
Mnoeo Christe 139
Mohr, Joseph 200
Monsell, John Samuel Bewley 72
Montgomery, James 23, 92, 204
Morgan, Patricia 54

Nazareth, Aniceto 22
Neale, John Mason 3, 9, 44, 57, 58, 88, 117, 122, 135, 161, 165, 169, 213, 236
Neander, Joachim 13, 191
Newbolt, Michael Robert 134
Newman, John Henry 74, 130, 190
Newton, John 18, 81, 104
Noel, Caroline Maria 29
Nun danket alle Gott 157
Nyberg, Anders 238
Nystrom, Martin 25

Oakeley, Frederick 160
Oakley, Charles Edward 282
Osler, Edward 189
Owens, Priscilla Jane 248

Paculabo, John 50
Perronet, Edward 10
Perry, Michael 167, 199
Pierpoint, Folliot Sandford 76
Plumptre, Edward Hayes 231
Pollock, Thomas Benson 66
Pott, Francis 24, 222
Prudentius, Aurelius Clemens 165
Puer nobis nascitur 237

Quincunque centum quaeritis 17

Redman, Matt 120
Rees, John 18
Richards, Hubert J. 86
Richards, Noel 233
Richards, Tricia 11
Rinkart, Martin 157
Rossetti, Christina Georgina 112
Rubin, Steffi Geiser 253
Ryecroft, Keith 50

Sandys, William 215
Santeuil, J. B. de 63
Saward, Michael 47
Schlegel, Katherina von 33
Schutte, Dan 114
Scottish Psalter, The 218
Scriven, Joseph Medlicott 243
Sears, Edmund Hamilton 113
Seddon, James Edward 87
Siena, Bianco da 51
Smith Jnr., Leonard E. 103
Smith, Henry 80
Smith, Walter Chalmers 109
Smyttan, George Hunt 77
South African traditional 238
Sparrow-Simpson, William John 8,
St Ambrose 182
St Bernard of Cluny 117
St Francis of Assisi 4
St Fulbert of Chartres 249
St Germanus 3
St John of Damascus 213
St Theodulph of Orleans 9
Stone, Samuel John 212
Struther, Jan 140
Surrexit hodie 121

Tate and Brady New Version 229
Tate, Nahum 247
Temple, Sebastian 147
Toplady, Augustus Montague 196
Townend Stuart 101
Traditional 79
Turner, Roy 14
Tuttle, Carl 100

Urbs beata Jerusalem 44

Vox clara ecce intonat 94

Wade, John Francis 160
Waring, Anna Laetitia 111
Watts, Isaac 53, 125, 168, 246
Weisse, Michael 46
Wesley, Charles 19, 48, 56, 91, 96, 118, 136, 143, 144, 164, 183, 194, 201, 251
Wesley, John 192
White, Henry Kirke 166
Whitefield, George 96
Whiting, William 65
Whittier, John Greenleaf 61, 110
Williams, Isaac 34, 63
Williams, Peter 90
Williams, William 90
Willis, Maria 67
Winkworth, Catherine 46, 157, 191
Woodward, George Ratcliffe 62, 226
Wordsworth, Christopher 6, 202

Young, John Freeman 200

Zschech, Darlene 153

Alphabetical Index of Tunes

Some modern tunes have not been given names. They will be found under the first line of text associated with them in the Index of First Lines.

Abends 207
Aberystwyth 118
Abridge 34
Adeste Fideles 160
Albano 162, 176
All for Jesus 8
All things bright and beautiful 16
Alton 74
Amazing grace 18
Angel voices 24
Aurelia 212
Aus der Tiefe (Heinlein) 77
Austria 81, 189

Bethany 155
Birjina gaztettobat zegoen 211
Bishopthorpe 110
Blaenwern 143
Blessed assurance 37
Bransle de L'Official 62
Bread of Heaven 39
Breslau 208
Bristol 95
Buckland 145
Bunessan 150

Caithness 163
Calypso Carol 199
Camberwell 29
Carlisle 40, 204
Christ triumphant 47
Contemplation 244
Corde natus
 (Divinum mysterium) 165
Cradle song 31
Cranham 112
Crimond 218
Cross of Jesus 56
Crucifer 134
Crüger 92
Cwm Rhondda 90

Darwell's 148th 250
Diademata 60
Dix 27
Dominus regit me 217
Doncaster 192
Down Ampney 51
Duke Street 72

Easter Hymn 121
Ellacombe 213
Ellers 197
England's Lane 76
Epiphany 41

Es ist ein' Ros' entsprungen 3
Evelyns 29
Eventide 2
Ewing 117

Faithfulness (Runyan) 89
Finlandia 33
Forest Green 171
Franconia 38
Fulda 239

Gelob't Sei Gott (Vulpius) 222
Gerontius 190
God be in my head 82
Golden Sheaves 235
Gopsal 194
Gwalchmai 129

Hanover 184
Harewood 45
Hatherop Castle 170
Heathlands 85
Helmsley 136
Here I am 114
Hereford 183
Herongate 115
Horsley 219
How great thou art 172
Humility (Oxford) 198
Hyfrydol 7

Irby 175
Iris 23

Jerusalem 20
Jesus is Lord 123
Jubilate Deo 127

Kings of Orient 242
Kingsfold 108
Knecht (Kocher) 169

Lasst uns erfreuen 4
Laudate Dominum (Parry) 180
Laus Deo (Redhead No. 46) 42
Little Cornard 98
Living God 203
Living Lord 138
Llanfair 91
Lobe den Herren 191
London New 84
Londonderry Air 106, 477
Lord of the years 137
Love Divine 143
Love unknown 154
Lübeck (Gott sei dank) 179
Luckington 132
Lux Benigna 130
Lux Eoi 6
Lyngham 164

Maccabaeus 223
Mannheim 131
Marching 230
Margaret 227
Melcombe 156
Melita 65
Mendelssohn 96
Merton 94, 119
Michael 13
Miles Lane 10
Misericordia 128
Monkland 133
Monks Gate 97
Montgomery 102
Morning Hymn 30
Morning Light 205
Moscow 228

Narenza 252
Nativity 53
Neander (Unser Herrscher) 57
Neighbour 245
Newington 224
Nicaea 99
Noel 113
Noel nouvelet 158
Nun danket 157

Ode to Joy 73
Old 104th 63
Old Hundredth 15
Oriel 236
O sacred head sore wounded 181

Paderborn 251
Passion chorale 181
Pastor pastorum 66
Penlan 111
Personent Hodie (Theodoric) 83
Petra (Redhead No. 76) 196
Praise, my soul 188
Puer nobis 237

Quam dilecta 240
Quem pastores 122

Ratisbon 48
Ravenshaw 142
Regent Square 135
Repton 61
Richmond 49, 190
Rievaulx 69
Rockingham 151, 246

Sagina 19
Salzburg 28
Sandon 130
Sandys 209
Savannah 144
Shine, Jesus, shine 141
Shipston 74

Sine Nomine 75
Siyahamba 238
Slane 35, 140
Southcote 178
Southwell (Damon) 139
Spiritus Vitae 159
St Agnes (Dykes) 126
St Albinus 124
St Andrew 119
St Anne 168
St Bernard 17
St Cecilia 232
St Clement 214
St Denio 109
St Edmund 202
St Ethelwald 201
St Francis Xavier 152
St Fulbert 249
St George's Windsor 59
St John Damascene 58
St Magnus 216
St Margaret 173
St Peter 104
St Theodulph 9
Stille Nacht 200
Strength and stay 182
Sussex 67
Sussex Carol 177

Tempus adest floridum 88
Thaxted 167
The first Nowell 215
This is your God 149
This joyful Eastertide
 (Vreuchten) 226
Thornbury 231
To God be the Glory 234
Truro 125

Unde et memores 21
University College 166

Veni Emmanuel 161
Veni, Creator Spiritus (Mechlin) 52
Veni, Sancte Spiritus 55

Wareham 193
Was lebet 185
Westminster Abbey 44
What a friend (Converse) 243
Will your anchor hold 248
Wiltshire 229
Winchester New 195
Wir pflügen 241
Wolvercote 170
Woodlands 210
Württemberg 46

Yanworth 87
Yorkshire (Stockport) 43

Metrical Index of Tunes

Some modern tunes, because of their free rhythmic patterns, are not listed in this index.

55 54 D
Bunessan   150

64 64 66 64
Bethany   155

65 65
Pastor pastorum   66

65 65 D
Evelyns   29
Camberwell   29

65 65 66 65
Monks Gate   97

66 11 D
Down Ampney   51

66 46 66 4
Moscow   228

66 65 D and Refrain
This is your God   149

66 66 44 44
Darwell's 148th   250
Harewood   45
Love unknown   154

66 66
Quam Dilecta   240
Ravenshaw   142
St Cecilia   232

66 66 and Refrain
Gopsal   194

666 66 and Refrain
Personent Hodie (Theodoric)   83

66 66 88
Little Cornard   98

66 8 D and Refrain
The old rugged cross   174

66 86
SM (Short Metre)
Carlisle   40, 204
Doncaster   192
Franconia   38
Narenza   252
Sandys   209
Southwell (Damon)   139
St Ethelwald   201

66 86 D
DSM (Double Short Metre)
Diademata   60

67 67 and Refrain
This joyful Eastertide (Vreuchten)   226

67 67 66 66
Nun danket   157

74 74 D
Gwalchmai   129

75 75 44 75
Living God   203

76 76
Knecht (Kocher)   169

76 76 and Refrain
All things bright and beautiful   16
St Theodulph   9

76 76 676
Es ist ein' Ros' entsprungen   3

76 76 D
Aurelia   212
Crüger   92
Ellacombe   213
Ewing   117
Hatherop Castle   170
Morning Light   205
Passion chorale   181
Penlan   111
St John Damascene   58
Tempus adest floridum   88
Thornbury   231
Wolvercote   170

76 76 D and Refrain
Wir pflügen   241

76 77
Puer nobis   237

77 74 D and Refrain
Here I am   114

77 77
Aus der Tiefe (Heinlein)   77
Buckland   145
Lübeck (Gott sei dank)   179
Monkland   133
Newington   224
Savannah   144
University College   166

77 77 and Alleluias
Easter Hymn   121
Llanfair   91
Württemberg   46

77 77 and Refrain
Bransle de L'Official   62
Humility (Oxford)   198

77 77 77
Bread of Heaven   39
Dix   27
England's Lane   76
Heathlands   85
Petra (Redhead No. 76)   196
Ratisbon   48

77 77 D
Aberystwyth   118
Salzburg   28
St Edmund   202
St George's Windsor   59

77 77 D and Refrain
Mendelssohn   96

777 D
Veni, Sancte Spiritus   55

78 78 and Alleluia
St Albinus   124

85 85 and Refrain
Christ triumphant   47

85 85 843
Angel voices   24

86 86
CM (Common Metre)
Abridge   34
Albano   162, 176
Amazing grace   18
Bishopthorpe   110
Bristol   95
Caithness   163
Contemplation   244
Crimond   218
Gerontius   190
Horsley   219
London New   84
Miles Lane   10
Nativity   53
Richmond   49, 190
St Agnes (Dykes)   126
St Anne   168
St Bernard   17
St Francis Xavier   152
St Fulbert   249
St Magnus   216
St Peter   104
Wiltshire   229
Winchester Old   247

86 86 Extended
CM (Common Metre) extended
Forest Green   171
Kingsfold   108
Lyngham   164
Noel   113

86 88 6
Repton   61

87 87
All for Jesus   8
Alton   74
Cross of Jesus   56
Dominus regit me   217
Love Divine   143
Marching   230
Merton   94
Shipston   74
St Andrew   119
Sussex   67

87 87 and refrain
Iris   23

87 87 33 7
Michael   13

87 87 47
Cwm Rhondda   90
Helmsley   136

87 87 77
Irby   175

87 87 87
Mannheim   131
Neander (Unser Herrscher)   57
Oriel   236

Praise, my soul   188
Regent Square   135
Westminster Abbey   44

87 87 87 7
Corde Natus (Divinum Mysterium)   165

87 87 D
Austria   81, 189
Blaenwern   143
Golden Sheaves   235
Hyfrydol   7
Lux Eoi   6
Ode to Joy   73
What a friend (Converse)   243

88 44 88 and Alleluias
Lasst uns erfreuen   4

88 86
Misericordia   128

88 86 and Refrain
Kings of Orient   242

88 87
Quem pastores   122

88 87 88 86
Jubilate Deo   127

888 and Alleluias
Gelobt sei Gott (Vulpius)   222

88 88
LM (Long Metre)
Abends   207
Breslau   208
Duke Street   72
Fulda   239
Hereford   183
Herongate   115
Melcombe   156
Morning Hymn   30
Old Hundredth   15
Rievaulx   69
Rockingham   151, 246
Truro   125
Veni, Creator Spiritus (Mechlin)   52
Wareham   193
Winchester New   195

88 88 and Refrain
LM (Long Metre) and Refrain
Veni Emmanuel   161

88 88 6
St Margaret   173

88 88 88
Melita   65
Sussex Carol   177

88 88 88 extended
Sagina   19

88 88 D
DLM (Double Long Metre)
Jerusalem   20

9 8 88 83
Living Lord   138

98 98
Spiritus Vitae 159
St Clement 214

99 79 and Refrain
Southcote 178

99 99 59 59
Siyahamba 238

9 9 10 10 6
Shine, Jesus, shine 141

10 4 10 4 10 10
Lux Benigna 130
Sandon 130

10 4 66 66 10 4
Luckington 132

10 8 11 8 and Refrain
Margaret 227

10 10 and Refrain
Crucifer 134

10 10 10 4
Sine Nomine 75

10 10 10 10
Ellers 197
Eventide 2
Slane 35
Woodlands 210
Yanworth 87

10 10 10 10 10 10
Finlandia 33
Unde et memores 21
Yorkshire (Stockport) 43

10 10 11 11
Hanover 184
Laudate Dominum
(Parry) 180
Paderborn 251

10 10 12 10
Birjina gaztettobat zegoen 211

10 11 11
Old 104th 63

10 11 11 11 and Refrain
Maccabaeus 223

10 11 11 12
Slane 140

11 10 11 10
Epiphany 41
Faithfulness (Runyan) 89
Lord of the years 137
Strength and stay 182

11 10 11 10 and Refrain
How great thou art 172

11 10 11 10 11 10 11 12
Londonderry Air 106

11 11 10 11
Noel Nouvelet 158

11 11 11 11
Cradle Song 31
Montgomery 102
St Denio 109

11 11 11 11 and Refrain
To God be the Glory 234

11 12 11 12 and Refrain
Jesus is Lord 123

11 12 12 10
Nicaea 99

13 10 and Refrain
Neighbour 245

13 10 13 10
Was lebet 185

13 13 13 13 13 13
Thaxted 167

14 14 4 7 8
Lobe den Herren 191

Irregular
Blessed assurance 37
Cranham 112
God be in my head 82
Stille Nacht 200
The first Nowell 215

Irregular and Refrain
Adeste Fideles 160
Calypso Carol 199
Will your anchor hold 248

Scriptural Index

GENESIS

1:1-4	Eternal Father, strong to save	65
	Lord, the light of your love	141
	O Breath of Life	159
	On this day, the first of days	179
	Thou, whose almighty word	228
1:1-5	Of the Father's love begotten	165
1:2-3	All over the world	14
2:7	Breathe on me, Breath of God	40
	O Breath of Life	159
3:14-15	Ye choirs of new Jerusalem	249
8:22	Great is thy faithfulness	89
	We plough the fields and scatter	241
11:9	It came upon the midnight clear	113
22:12	O Lord, my God	172
28:10-19	Blessed assurance, Jesus is mine	37
	Nearer, my God, to thee	155
49:24	Rock of ages	196

EXODUS

3:5	Be still, for the presence of the Lord	32
3:15	The head that once was crowned with thorns	216
12:11	The day of resurrection	213
12:13	At the Lamb's high feast we sing	28
12:21	At the Lamb's high feast we sing	28
13:21	Glorious things of thee are spoken	81
	Guide me, O thou great Redeemer	90
	Through the night of doubt and sorrow	230
14:28	At the Lamb's high feast we sing	28
	Come, ye faithful, raise the strain	58
16	At the Lamb's high feast we sing	28
16:4	At the Lamb's high feast we sing	28
	Glorious things of thee are spoken	81
	Guide me, O thou great Redeemer	90
19:1-25	O come, O come, Emmanuel	161
20:3	Make way, make way	148
33:22	Rock of ages	196
34:6	Praise, my soul, the King of heaven	188

LEVITICUS

6:13	O thou who camest from above	183
16:2-15	Once, only once, and once for all	176

NUMBERS

14:18	Praise, my soul, the King of heaven	188

DEUTERONOMY

5:7	Make way, make way	148
10:17	Alleluia, sing to Jesus	7
26:9-11	To thee, O Lord, our hearts we raise	235
33:27	Fight the good fight	72

JOSHUA

3:7	Guide me, O thou great Redeemer	90
3:14-17	Thine be the glory	223
	This joyful Eastertide	226
6:20	Disposer supreme	63

2 SAMUEL

7:16	Rejoice, the Lord is King	194
	The day thou gavest, Lord, is ended	214
22:2	For all the saints	75
23:5	Put thou thy trust in God	192

1 KINGS

8:27	In the bleak mid-winter	112
8:30-40	Christ is made the sure foundation	44
19:9-18	Dear Lord and Father of mankind	61

2 KINGS

2:11	And did those feet in ancient time	20

JOB

29:16	Come, thou Holy Spirit, come	55
38:7-11	Angels from the realms of glory	23
	Eternal Father, strong to save	65
	O little town of Bethlehem	171

PSALMS

2:1-2	My song is love unknown	154
2:8	I cannot tell	106
2:9	Thy kingdom come, O God	232
3:3	As the deer pants for the water	25
4:8	This joyful Eastertide	226
8:1-9	O Lord, my God	172
8:2	Jesus shall reign	125
8:3	Fill your hearts with joy and gladness	73
8:5	Be thou my guardian and my guide	34
10:14	Abide with me	2
16:5	Amazing grace	18
	Be thou my vision	35
	Jerusalem the golden	117
16:9	This joyful Eastertide	226
18:2	For all the saints	75
	Rock of ages	196
18:2-3	For all the saints	75
18:5	Be thou my guardian and my guide	34
18:11	Put thou thy trust in God	192
19:1	All heaven declares	11
19:10	As the deer pants for the water	25
23	The Lord's my shepherd	218
23:1-6	Abide with me	2
	Faithful Shepherd, feed me	66
	In heavenly love abiding	111
	The King of love my shepherd is	217
24:7	King of glory, King of peace	129
	Make way, make way	148
24:7-10	For all the saints	75
	Hail the day that sees him rise	91
25:2	Jesu, lover of my soul	118
26:8	We love the place, O God	240
27:1	Abide with me	2
27:6	Put thou thy trust in God	192
28:7	Guide me, O thou great Redeemer	90
31:1	Jesu, lover of my soul	118
31:2-3	For all the saints	75
31:3	Abide with me	2
	For all the saints	75
31:5	Father, I place into your hands	68
33:9	Of the Father's love begotten	165
33:12	Lord, for the years	137
33:20	O God, our help in ages past	168
34:1-22	Through all the changing scenes of life	229
36:6	Immortal, invisible, God only wise	109
36:9	Jesu, lover of my soul	118
40:1	Good King Wenceslas	88
40:2	Jesu, lover of my soul	118
42:1-11	All my hope on God is founded	13
	As the deer pants for the water	25
44:3	Thy hand, O God, has guided	231
45:6	Hail to the Lord's anointed	92
	The day thou gavest, Lord, is ended	214
46:1	Immortal love, for ever full	110
	O God, our help in ages past	168
46:1-11	Glorious things of thee are spoken	81
46:2	Abide with me	2
46:10	Be still, for the presence of the Lord	32
	Be still, my soul	33
48:1-14	Glorious things of thee are spoken	81
48:3	O God, our help in ages past	168

48:10	Thy hand, O God, has guided	231
48:14	Abide with me	2
55:1-2	All creatures of our God and King	6
55:17	Praise him, praise him, praise him in the morning	187
57:1	Jesu, lover of my soul	118
57:8	Crown him with many crowns	60
57:10	Great is thy faithfulness	89
62:2	For all the saints	75
65	Fill your hearts with joy and gladness	73
65:1	Come, ye faithful, raise the anthem	57
65:7	Eternal Father, strong to save	65
65:13	To thee, O Lord, our hearts we raise	235
66:1-3	My Jesus, my Saviour	153
67:1-7	God of mercy, God of grace	85
68:4	God moves in a mysterious way	84
68:33	God moves in a mysterious way	84
71:3	For all the saints	75
72:1-19	Hail to the Lord's anointed	92
	Jesus shall reign	125
72:7	It came upon the midnight clear	113
73:24	Abide with me	2
78:24-25	Alleluia, sing to Jesus	7
	Bread of heaven, on thee we feed	39
	Guide me, O thou great Redeemer	90
	My God, and is thy table spread	151
81:16	I, the Lord of sea and sky	114
84:2	Alleluia, alleluia, give thanks to the risen Lord	5
84:7	Soldiers of Christ, arise	201
85:8-13	Fill your hearts with joy and gladness	73
	We love the place, O God	240
86:9	Angels from the realms of glory	23
86:13	Great is thy faithfulness	89
86:15	Praise, my soul, the King of heaven	188
87:1-3	City of God, how broad and far	49
	Glorious things of thee are spoken	81
	Light's abode, celestial Salem	135
88:9	Oft in danger, oft in woe	166
89:15	The Spirit lives to set us free	221
90	O God, our help in ages past	168
91:2	All my hope on God is founded	13
	For all the saints	75
	God is our strength and refuge	219
91:4	Jesu, lover of my soul	118
92:4	My Jesus, my Saviour	153
92:5	O Lord, my God	172
93:1	How lovely on the mountains	103
95:2	Guide me, O thou great Redeemer	90
96:1	My Jesus, my Saviour	153
96:11	My Jesus, my Saviour	153
97:1	Rejoice, the Lord is King	194
97:2	Put thou thy trust in God	192
97:5	My Jesus, my Saviour	153
98:4	My Jesus, my Saviour	153
98:8	A great and mighty wonder	3
100:1-5	All people that on earth do dwell	15
	Jubilate, everybody	127
100:4	I will enter his gates	116
102:19	Praise to the Holiest	190
102:27	O God, our help in ages past	168
103:8	Praise, my soul, the King of heaven	188
103:11	Great is thy faithfulness	89
103:13	How deep the Father's love for us	101
103:20	Angel-voices ever singing	24
104	O worship the King	184
104:9	Eternal Father, strong to save	65
104:14	Fill your hearts with joy and gladness	73
104:30	Breathe on me, Breath of God	40
104:31	Angel-voices ever singing	24
105:40	Guide me, O thou great Redeemer	90
	My God, and is thy table spread	151
107:23-32	Lead us, heavenly Father, lead us	131
110:1	Rejoice, the Lord is King	194
	Ye choirs of new Jerusalem	249
116:17	All my hope on God is founded	13
117:1-2	Great is thy faithfulness	89
118:6	Abide with me	2
118:19-24	I will enter his gates	116
	This is the day	225

118:22	Christ is made the sure foundation	44
118:25-26	Hosanna, hosanna	100
119:57	Amazing grace	18
119:114	How sweet the name of Jesus sounds	104
121:3	All my hope on God is founded	13
124:8	O God, our help in ages past	168
126:6	Come, ye faithful, raise the strain	58
136	All my hope on God is founded	13
139:23	Lord, the light of your love	141
140:4	Be thou my guardian and my guide	34
145:8	Praise, my soul, the King of heaven	188
146:10	Come, ye faithful, raise the anthem	57
147:3	I cannot tell	106
	Listen to my voice	403
147:4-18	Fill your hearts with joy and gladness	73
147:12	Come, ye faithful, raise the anthem	57
147:16	We plough the fields and scatter	241
147:18	Breathe on me, Breath of God	40
	Lord, the light of your love	141
148	O praise ye the Lord!	180
	Praise the Lord, ye heavens adore him	189
148:2	Angel-voices ever singing	24
	Ye holy angels bright	250
148:3	Praise, my soul, the King of heaven	188
149:1-2	Of the Father's love begotten	165
149:2	Come, ye faithful, raise the anthem	57
150	O praise ye the Lord!	180
150:6	Praise to the Lord, the Almighty	191

PROVERBS

9:5	My God, and is thy table spread	151
14:34	Lord, for the years	137

SONG OF SOLOMON

8:6	At the name of Jesus	29

ISAIAH

2:4-5	We are marching	238
6:1-3	Bright the vision that delighted	42
	Immortal, invisible, God only wise	109
	Lord, the light of your love	141
6:2-3	Crown him with many crowns	60
	Holy, holy, holy! Lord God almighty	99
6:8-9	I, the Lord of sea and sky	114
7:4	Fight the good fight	72
7:14	Hark, the herald angels sing	96
	O come, O come, Emmanuel	161
9:1-2	Lord, the light of your love	141
	Thy kingdom come, O God	232
9:5-6	Crown him with many crowns	60
	Hark, the herald angels sing	96
	Unto us a boy is born	237
9:6	Hark, the glad sound	95
	King of glory, King of peace	129
	Rejoice, the Lord is King	194
11:1-2	Come, Holy Ghost, our souls inspire	52
	Come, thou Holy Spirit, come	55
	O come, O come, Emmanuel	161
11:1-9	All over the world	14
11:10	Crown him with many crowns	60
14:12	Christ, whose glory fills the skies	48
16:1	Hark! a herald voice is calling	94
	See, amid the winter's snow	198
22:2	O come, O come, Emmanuel	161
33:20-21	Glorious things of thee are spoken	81
40:1	Lord, thy word abideth	142
40:1-11	Do not be afraid	64
40:5	I cannot tell	106
40:7-8	Immortal, invisible, God only wise	109
40:7-9	Lord, thy word abideth	142
40:11	Praise, my soul, the King of heaven	188
40:26	Fill your hearts with joy and gladness	73
42:1-3	How firm a foundation	102
43:1-4	Do not be afraid	64
43:11	All for Jesus!	8

52:3	From heaven you came	78
52:7-10	How firm a foundation	102
53	How lovely on the mountains	103
53:1-12	Christ triumphant	47
53:4-5	How deep the Father's love for us	101
53:4-7	The strife is o'er, the battle done	222
	What a friend we have in Jesus	243
53:12	Bread of heaven, on thee we feed	39
55:3	Put thou thy trust in God	192
55:12	You shall go out with joy	253
56:5	The head that once was crowned with thorns	216
61:1-3	Come, Holy Ghost, our souls inspire	52
	Hail to the Lord's anointed	92
	Hark, the glad sound	95
	I cannot tell	106
	Lord, for the years	137
	Make way, make way	148
	O for a thousand tongues to sing	164
66:1	Alleluia, sing to Jesus	7

JEREMIAH

| 51:46 | Fight the good fight | 72 |

LAMENTATIONS

| 3:23 | New every morning is the love | 156 |

EZEKIEL

1:26	Come, ye faithful, raise the anthem	57
	Ride on, ride on in majesty	195
11:23	Love divine, all loves excelling	143
36:25-26	All over the world	14
	I, the Lord of sea and sky	114
37	Breathe on me, Breath of God	40

DANIEL

2:22	God moves in a mysterious way	84
3:52:90	All creatures of our God and King	4
7:9	Come, ye faithful, raise the anthem	57
	Crown him with many crowns	60
	O worship the King	184
7:9-22	Immortal, invisible, God only wise	109
7:10	Angel-voices ever singing	24
	Come, let us join our cheerful songs	53

HOSEA

| 13:4 | All for Jesus! | 8 |

JOEL

| 2:28 | All over the world | 14 |

HABAKKUK

| 2:14 | All over the world | 14 |

HAGGAI

| 2:7 | Angels from the realms of glory | 23 |
| | Come, thou long-expected Jesus | 56 |

MALACHI

3:1	Angels from the realms of glory	23
3:6	Abide with me	2
	Great is thy faithfulness	89
4:2	Christ, whose glory fills the skies	48
	Hark, the herald-angels sing	96
	O come, O come, Emmanuel	161

MATTHEW

| 1:23 | Hark, the herald-angels sing | 96 |
| | Morning has broken | 150 |

	O little town of Bethlehem	171
	The angel Gabriel from heaven came	211
2:1-12	A great and mighty wonder	3
	Angels from the realms of glory	23
	As with gladness men of old	27
	Brightest and best of the suns	41
	Crown him with many crowns	60
	In the bleak mid-winter	112
	O come, all ye faithful	160
	See him lying on a bed of straw	199
	The first Nowell	215
	We three kings of Orient are	242
2:11	O worship the Lord in the beauty of holiness	185
2:13-18	Unto us a boy is born	237
3:11	All over the world	14
4:1-11	Forty days and forty nights	77
	Lead us, heavenly Father, lead us	131
4:16-17	Lord, the light of your love	141
4:18-22	Dear Lord and Father of mankind	61
	Jesus calls us: o'er the tumult	119
4:21	I danced in the morning	107
5:3-4	The Church's one foundation	212
5:5	Fill your hearts with joy and gladness	73
	Make way, make way	148
5:8	Blest are the pure in heart	38
	The Spirit lives to set us free	221
6:9-13	Make me a channel of your peace	147
	Thy kingdom come, O God	232
	We plough the fields and scatter	241
6:10	Lord, for the years	137
6:31-33	Lord, for the years	137
7:11	We plough the fields and scatter	241
7:13	And now, O Father, mindful of the love	21
	A new commandment	22
	Faithful Shepherd, feed me	66
	Loving Shepherd of thy sheep	145
7:14	As with gladness men of old	27
8:11	The Spirit lives to set us free	221
8:17	What a friend we have in Jesus	243
8:20	Thou didst leave thy throne	227
8:23-27	Eternal Father, strong to save	65
	I cannot tell	106
8:26	Be still, my soul	33
9:21	Immortal love, for ever full	110
10:8-9	God's Spirit is in my heart	86
10:38	Lift high the cross	134
	Take up thy cross, the Saviour said	208
11:5	My song is love unknown	154
11:17	I danced in the morning	107
11:19	Alleluia, sing to Jesus	7
11:28-30	All ye who seek a comfort sure	17
	I cannot tell	106
	I heard the voice of Jesus say	108
	Love divine, all loves excelling	143
12:21	Come, thou long-expected Jesus	56
12:29	Christ the Lord is risen again	46
13:4-9	We plough the fields and scatter	241
13:25	Come, ye thankful people come	59
13:39	Alleluia, alleluia, hearts to heaven and voices raise	6
13:41	At the name of Jesus	29
	Come, ye thankful people come	59
13:55	Lord of all hopefulness	140
14:22-23	Eternal Father, strong to save	65
15:30-31	My song is love unknown	154
16:24	Take up thy cross, the Saviour said	208
18:12	Amazing grace	18
	The King of love my shepherd is	217
20:28	From heaven you came	78
	Jesus is Lord! Creation's voice proclaims it	123
21:1-11	All glory, laud and honour	9
21:8-9	Give me joy in my heart	79
	Hark, the glad sound	95
	Hosanna, hosanna	100
	My song is love unknown	154
	Ride on, ride on in majesty	195
22:1-10	Thy hand, O God, has guided	231
22:45	Hail to the Lord's anointed	92
24:30	Hark! a herald voice is calling	94

24:30-31	Lo, he comes with clouds descending	136
	O Lord, my God	172
	This joyful Eastertide	226
24:42-44	Come, thou long-expected Jesus	56
	Ye servants of the Lord	252
25:1-13	Give me joy in my heart	79
25:31	At the name of Jesus	29
25:31-46	When I needed a neighbour	245
26:36-46	From heaven you came	78
26:41	Be thou my guardian and my guide	34
27:22	My song is love unknown	154
27:26	My song is love unknown	154
27:29	O dearest Lord, thy sacred head	162
	O sacred head sore wounded	181
	The head that once was crowned with thorns	216
27:66	Love's redeeming work is done	144
27:39-44	How deep the Father's love for us	101
28:1-10	On this day, the first of days	179
	Thine be the glory	223
28:9	The day of resurrection	213
28:18-19	Go forth and tell	87
28:20	Alleluia, sing to Jesus	7

MARK

1:8	All over the world	14
1:12	Lead us, heavenly Father, lead us	131
1:12-13	Forty days and forty nights	77
1:16-20	Dear Lord and Father of mankind	61
	Jesus calls us: o'er the tumult	119
1:24	There is a Redeemer	220
2:14	On Christmas night all Christians sing	177
3:27	Christ the Lord is risen again	46
3:28	Immortal love, for ever full	110
4:3-9	We plough the fields and scatter	241
4:26-29	Come, ye thankful people, come	59
	I cannot tell	106
	Now the green blade riseth	158
4:35-41	Be still, my soul	33
	Eternal Father, strong to save	65
	I cannot tell	106
6:3	Lord of all hopefulness	140
6:45-52	Eternal Father, strong to save	65
7:37	All things bright and beautiful	16
8:34	Lift high the cross	134
	Take up thy cross, the Saviour said	208
8:38	At the name of Jesus	29
10:45	From heaven you came	78
	Jesus is Lord! Creations voice proclaims it	123
11:1-11	All glory, laud and honour	9
11:8-10	Give me joy in my heart	79
	Hark, the glad sound	95
	Hosanna, hosanna	100
	My song is love unknown	154
	Ride on, ride on in majesty	195
12:37	Hail to the Lord's anointed	92
13:11	God's Spirit is in my heart	86
13:25-26	Lo, he comes with clouds descending	136
	O Lord, my God	172
13:26	Hark! a herald voice is calling	94
13:37	Ye servants of the Lord	252
14:32-42	From heaven you came	78
14:38	Be thou my guardian and my guide	34
15:13	My song is love unknown	154
15:15-17	My song is love unknown	154
	O dearest Lord, thy sacred head	162
	O sacred head sore wounded	181
15:17-20	The head that once was crowned with thorns	216
15:33-34	How deep the Father's love for us	101
16:1-8	On this day, the first of days	179
	Thine be the glory	223
16:4	Love's redeeming work is done	144

LUKE

1-2	The angel Gabriel from heaven came	211
1:26-38	Of the Father's love begotten	165
1:32	Jerusalem the golden	117

1:33	Crown him with many crowns	60
	Rejoice, the Lord is King	194
	The day thou gavest, Lord, is ended	214
1:35	There is a Redeemer	220
1:46:55	Tell out, my soul	210
1:51-52	Fill your hearts with joy and gladness	73
1:78	Christ, whose glory fills the skies	48
2:1-7	Once in royal David's city	175
2:1-20	Christians, awake!	43
	Crown him with many crowns	60
	See, amid the winter's snow	198
	See him lying on a bed of straw	199
	Silent night	200
2:5-7	Once in royal David's city	175
2:7	Away in a manger	31
	Brightest and best of the suns	41
	I cannot tell	106
	Jesus, good above all other	122
	Thou didst leave thy throne	227
	Unto us a boy is born	237
	We have a gospel to proclaim	239
2:8-14	A great and mighty wonder	3
	Angels from the realms of glory	23
2:8-20	In the bleak midwinter	112
	O come, all ye faithful	160
	The first Nowell	215
	While shepherds watched	247
2:11	My Jesus, my Saviour	153
2:13-14	Ding dong, merrily on high	62
	It came upon the midnight clear	113
	O little town of Bethlehem	171
2:14	Alleluia, alleluia, hearts to heaven and voices raise	6
	Angels from the realms of glory	23
	Ding dong! merrily on high	62
	Hark, the herald-angels sing	267
	On Christmas night all Christians sing	177
2:25	Come, thou long-expected Jesus	56
3:16	All over the world	14
4:1-13	Forty days and forty nights	77
	Lead us, heavenly Father, lead us	131
4:18	God's Spirit is in my heart	86
	Hail to the Lord's anointed	92
	Make way, make way	148
	O for a thousand tongues to sing	164
4:18-19	Hark, the glad sound	95
	Lord, for the years	137
4:34	Be still, my soul	33
	There is a Redeemer	220
5:11-12	Dear Lord and Father of mankind	61
6:21	Make way, make way	148
7:22	My song is love unknown	154
	Thou, whose almighty word	228
7:34	Alleluia, sing to Jesus	7
7:37	I danced in the morning	107
8:5-8	We have a gospel to proclaim	239
8:22-25	Be still, my soul	33
	Eternal Father, strong to save	65
	I cannot tell	106
8:44	Immortal love, for ever full	110
9:23	Lift high the cross	134
	Take up thy cross, the Saviour said	208
9:26	At the name of Jesus	29
9:58	Thou didst leave thy throne	227
10:34	When I needed a neighbour	245
10:39	To be in your presence	233
11:1	Lord Jesus Christ	138
11:2-4	Make me a channel of your peace	147
	Thy kingdom come, O God	232
	We plough the fields and scatter	241
11:22	Christ the Lord is risen again	46
12:35	Ye servants of the Lord	252
12:40	Come, thou long-expected Jesus	56
13:10-17	I danced in the morning	107
13:24	As with gladness men of old	27
	Faithful Shepherd, feed me	66
	Loving Shepherd of thy sheep	145
14:12-24	I, the Lord of sea and sky	114
14:16-24	Thy hand, O God, has guided	231

15:4-6	Amazing grace	18
	The King of love my shepherd is	217
15:24	Christ the Lord is risen again	46
19:10	The Spirit lives to set us free	221
19:28-38	All glory, laud and honour	9
	My song is love unknown	154
19:37-38	Ride on, ride on in majesty	195
20:21	God's Spirit is in my heart	86
20:44	Hail to the Lord's anointed	92
21:27	Hark! a herald voice is calling	94
21:36	Ye servants of the Lord	252
22:19-20	Amazing grace	18
	Lord Jesus Christ	138
22:40-46	From heaven you came	78
22:60-61	O sacred head sore wounded	181
23:21	My song is love unknown	154
23:34	All ye who seek a comfort sure	17
	Meekness and majesty	149
24:1-8	On this day, the first of days	179
	Thine be the glory	223
24:2	Love's redeeming work is done	144
24:9	Abide with me	2
24:36-43	As we are gathered	26
24:49-52	Be still, for the presence of the Lord	32

JOHN

1:1	Lord, for the years	137
1:1-14	At the name of Jesus	29
	Of the Father's love begotten	165
1:9-10	Lead, kindly light	130
1:10	My song is love unknown	154
1:14	A great and mighty wonder	3
	Be thou my vision	35
	Christians, awake!	43
	Christ triumphant	47
	Come, ye faithful, raise the anthem	57
	Crown him with many crowns	60
	Hark, the herald-angels sing	96
	My song is love unknown	154
	O come, all ye faithful	160
	We have a gospel to proclaim	239
1:29	And did those feet in ancient time	20
	Christ the Lord is risen again	46
	Hail the day that sees him rise	91
	Hark! a herald voice is calling	94
	Just as I am, without one plea	128
	On a hill far away	174
	There is a Redeemer	220
1:35-39	Dear Lord and Father of mankind	61
1:51	Blessed assurance, Jesus is mine	37
3:3	Hark, the herald-angels sing	96
	I cannot tell	106
3:8	Breathe on me, Breath of God	40
3:16	From heaven you came	78
	Hallelujah, my Father	93
	To God be the glory!	234
4:14	I heard the voice of Jesus say	108
	Jesu, lover of my soul	118
4:35	O Breath of Life	159
4:42	I cannot tell	106
	Jesu, the very thought of thee	126
	My Jesus, my Saviour	153
	Of the Father's love begotten	165
5:3	Thou, whose almighty word	228
5:9	I danced in the morning	107
5:28	O for a thousand tongues to sing	164
	The Spirit lives to set us free	221
6:16-21	Eternal Father, strong to save	65
6:31	My God, and is thy table spread	151
6:31-32	Guide me, O thou great Redeemer	90
6:48	Oft in danger, oft in woe	166
	To thee, O Lord, our hearts we raise	235
6:50-52	I danced in the morning	107
6:51-55	Bread of heaven, on thee we feed	39
6:68	My Jesus, my Saviour	153
6:69	Be still, for the presence of the Lord	32
	There is a Redeemer	220

7:37-38	Breathe on me, Breath of God	40
8:12	Christ, whose glory fills the skies	48
	Colours of day	50
	For all the saints	75
	I heard the voice of Jesus say	108
	Lead, kindly light	130
	Lord, the light of your love	141
	The Spirit lives to set us free	221
	Thou, whose almighty word	228
8:32	God is love: his the care	83
	Lord, the light of your love	141
	Thou didst leave thy throne	227
9:1-41	Amazing grace	18
10:11-16	All for Jesus!	8
	How sweet the name of Jesus sounds	104
	I cannot tell	106
	O sacred head sore wounded	181
	Thine for ever! God of love	224
10:11-18	Loving Shepherd of thy sheep	145
10:28	Loving Shepherd of thy sheep	145
11:25-27	Breathe on me, Breath of God	40
	I danced in the morning	107
	Love's redeeming work is done	144
11:43	The Spirit lives to set us free	221
12:12-15	All glory, laud and honour	9
12:13	Give me joy in my heart	79
	Hark, the glad sound	95
	Hosanna, hosanna	100
	My song is love unknown	154
	Ride on, ride on in majesty	195
12:26	O Jesus, I have promised	170
12:28	Father, we love you	70
12:31-32	Lift high the cross	134
12:35	The Spirit lives to set us free	221
13:1-15	Meekness and majesty	149
13:34-35	A new commandment	22
	Peace, perfect peace, is the gift	186
14:2	Hail the day that sees him rise	91
14:3	O Jesus, I have promised	170
14:6	Fight the good fight	72
	How sweet the name of Jesus sounds	104
	Thine for ever! God of love	224
14:16	The Spirit lives to set us free	221
14:18	Alleluia, sing to Jesus	7
14:26	Come, thou Holy Spirit, come	55
	O King enthroned on high	504
14:27	Peace, perfect peace, is the gift	186
	Saviour, again to thy dear name we raise	197
15:1-17	A new commandment	22
15:4-5	Abide with me	2
15:7	I danced in the morning	107
16:20	Come, ye faithful, raise the strain	58
17:21	As we are gathered	26
17:24	O Jesus, I have promised	170
18:11	Praise to the Holiest	190
18:37	God is love: his the care	83
18:40	My song is love unknown	154
19:2	O dearest Lord, thy sacred head	162
	O sacred head sore wounded	181
	The head that once was crowned with thorns	216
19:6	My song is love unknown	154
19:20	There is a green hill far away	219
19:25	O sacred head sore wounded	181
19:30	How deep the Father's love for us	101
19:34	At the Lamb's high feast we sing	28
	O dearest Lord, thy sacred head	162
	Rock of ages	196
20:1-10	Love's redeeming work is done	144
	On this day, the first of days	179
	Thine be the glory	223
20:19	Saviour, again to thy dear name we raise	197
	The day of resurrection	213
	Thine be the glory	223
20:19-31	As we are gathered	26
20:21-22	Breathe on me, Breath of God	40
	God's Spirit is in my heart	86
20:26-29	Crown him with many crowns	60
	From heaven you came	78

	My God, I love thee	152
	O dearest Lord, thy sacred head	162
20:27-28	Hail the day that sees him rise	91
	There is a green hill far away	219

ACTS

1:4-5	All over the world	20
1:6-11	Alleluia, sing to Jesus	12
	Hail the day that sees him rise	91
1:8	Be still, for the presence of the Lord	32
1:11	At the name of Jesus	29
	Once in royal David's city	175
2:1-4	Come down, O Love divine	51
	Come, Holy Ghost, our souls inspire	52
	Father, hear the prayer we offer	67
	Lord, the light of your love	141
	O Breath of Life	159
	On this day, the first of days	179
	Spirit of the living God	203
2:15	Now the green blade riseth	158
2:18	All over the world	14
2:23	To the name of our salvation	236
2:24	At the Lamb's high feast we sing	28
	Come, ye faithful, raise the strain	58
	We have a gospel to proclaim	239
2:34	Rejoice, the Lord is King	194
3:8	O for a thousand tongues to sing	164
3:15	My song is love unknown	154
	Thine be the glory	223
4:2	O for a thousand tongues to sing	164
4:11	Christ is made the sure foundation	44
4:12	All hail the power of Jesus' name	10
	To the name of our salvation	236
7:48-49	Alleluia, sing to Jesus	7
	Praise to the Holiest	190
10:38	Thou, whose almighty word	228
12:7	And can it be	19
20:29	Thy kingdom come, O God	232

ROMANS

4:5	Christ triumphant	47
5:1-2	I am a new creation	105
5:6	Abide with me	2
5:8	Come on and celebrate!	54
5:10	From heaven you came	78
	Hark, the herald-angels sing	95
	My God, I love thee	152
6:9	I danced in the morning	107
6:18	On Christmas night all Christians sing	177
8:1	And can it be	19
	I am a new creation	105
8:1-3	The Spirit lives to set us free	221
8:9	The Spirit lives to set us free	221
8:11	Alleluia, give thanks to the risen Lord	5
8:15	Abba, Father, let me be	1
8:21-22	On Christmas night all Christians sing	177
8:31-19	Hail the day that sees him rise	91
8:31-39	Jesus lives! thy terrors now	124
8:32	O Lord, my God	172
8:34	And now, O Father, mindful of the love	21
8:37	Soldiers of Christ, arise	201
	Thine be the glory	223
10:9	Alleluia, alleluia, give thanks to the risen Lord	5
10:14	Go forth and tell	87
11:33-36	Meekness and majesty	149
12:1-2	Lord, for the years	137
15:12	O come, O come, Emmanuel	161

1 CORINTHIANS

1:18-30	How deep the Father's love for us	101
1:25-27	Be thou my vision	35
1:28	Disposer supreme	63
3:6	We plough the fields and scatter	241
3:9	Come, ye thankful people, come	59
3:11	Christ is made the sure foundation	44
	The Church's one foundation	212

5:7	Christ the Lord is risen again	46
5:7-8	At the Lamb's high feast we sing	28
6:20	Bind us together, Lord	36
	Blessed assurance, Jesus is mine	37
	The Church's one foundation	212
7:23	There is a green hill far away	219
9:24	Fight the good fight	72
9:24-27	Fight the good fight	72
10:4	Rock of ages	196
10:24	From heaven you came	78
11:23-25	Amazing grace	18
	Lord Jesus Christ	138
11:26	Once, only once, and once for all	176
12:3	Jesus is Lord	123
	Lord Jesus Christ	138
12:3-4	Alleluia, give thanks to the risen Lord	5
12:12	Bind us together, Lord	36
13:4-8	A new commandment	22
13:7	Father, I place into your hands	68
13:12	Loving Shepherd of thy sheep	145
15:4-7	Now the green blade riseth	158
15:14	This joyful Eastertide	226
15:20	Alleluia, alleluia, hearts to heaven and voices raise	6
	Blessed assurance, Jesus is mine	37
	Hail the day that sees him rise	91
15:45	Praise to the Holiest	190
15:52	This joyful Eastertide	226
15:54-57	Jesus lives! thy terrors now	124
	Lift high the Cross	134
15:55	Love's redeeming work is done	144
15:55-57	Abide with me	2
	Bind us together, Lord	36
	Thine be the glory	223

2 CORINTHIANS

3:17	The Spirit lives to set us free	221
3:17-18	Lord, the light of your love	141
	Love divine, all loves excelling	143
4:6	Lord, the light of your love	141
4:7	Disposer supreme	63
5:7-8	O God, our help in ages past	168
5:17	I am a new creation	105
	Love divine, all loves excelling	143
	The Church's one foundation	212
6:10	Give thanks with a grateful heart	80
12:10	Give thanks with a grateful heart	80

GALATIANS

2:19-20	Alleluia, give thanks to the risen Lord	5
	Come on and celebrate!	54
	From heaven you came	78
2:20	Alleluia, alleluia, give thanks to the risen Lord	5
	Lord, for the years	137
4:5-7	Blessed assurance, Jesus is mine	37
4:6	Abba, Father, let me be	1
6:14	Lord, for the years	137
6:14-15	Love divine, all loves excelling	143
	When I survey the wondrous cross	246

EPHESIANS

1:21-23	Of the Father's love begotten	165
2:12	All for Jesus!	8
2:13-22	Bread of heaven, on thee we feed	39
	Christ is made the sure foundation	44
	Christ is our cornerstone	45
3:12	And can it be	19
	Blessed assurance, Jesus is mine	37
3:17	Bread of heaven, on thee we feed	39
3:18	Just as I am, without one plea	128
3:19	All my hope on God is founded	13
4:5	The Church's one foundation	212
	Thy hand, O God, has guided	231
4:24	And can it be	19
5:1-2	Come on and celebrate!	54
	On Christmas night all Christians sing	177

5:6-20	Awake, my soul, and with the sun	30
5:8	The Spirit lives to set us free	221
5:8-14	Hark! a herald voice is calling	94
6:10-17	Be thou my vision	35
6:10-18	Soldiers of Christ, arise	201

PHILIPPIANS

2:4	From heaven you came	78
2:5-11	At the name of Jesus	29
	Meekness and majesty	149
	Praise to the Holiest	190
2:6-11	Jesus Christ	120
2:7	And can it be	19
	Blest are the pure in heart	38
	Christ triumphant	47
	Hark, the herald-angels sing	95
	Thou didst leave thy throne	227
2:10-11	Alleluia, give thanks to the risen Lord	5
	How lovely on the mountains	103
	Jesus is Lord! Creation's voice proclaims it	123
2:11	For all the saints	75
	To the name of our salvation	236
3:7-8	When I survey the wondrous cross	246
3:8-12	All I once held dear	12
3:9	And now, O Father, mindful of the love	21
3:12-14	Fight the good fight	72

COLOSSIANS

1:13-20	Of the Father's love begotten	165
1:15	Meekness and majesty	149
1:16	At the name of Jesus	29
1:18	Hail the day that sees him rise	91
1:27	Lord, for the years	137
2:3	All my hope on God is founded	13
2:7	Bread of heaven, on thee we feed	39
3:14	Bind us together, Lord	36
	Come down, O Love divine	51

1 THESSALONIANS

| 2:19 | Fight the good fight | 72 |
| 4:16 | This joyful Eastertide | 226 |

2 THESSALONIANS

| 1:7 | At the name of Jesus | 29 |
| 2:10 | God is love: his the care | 83 |

1 TIMOTHY

1:17	Immortal, invisible, God only wise	109
	Meekness and majesty	149
4:10	All my hope on God is founded	13
6:12	Fight the good fight	72

2 TIMOTHY

1:10	My Jesus, my Saviour	153
3:14-17	Lord, for the years	137
4:7	Fight the good fight	72
	For all the saints	75

TITUS

| 3:4 | The Spirit lives to set us free | 221 |

HEBREWS

1:3	Meekness and majesty	149
	Rejoice, the Lord is King	194
1:8	The day thou gavest, Lord, is ended	214
2:9	All hail the power of Jesus' name	10
	Be still, for the presence of the Lord	32
2:9-10	How deep the Father's love for us	101
4:14	How sweet the name of Jesus sounds	104
4:15	At the Lamb's high feast we sing	28

4:16	Blessed assurance, Jesus is mine	37
5:8	Meekness and majesty	149
7:25	And now, O Father, mindful of the love	21
	Hail the day that sees him rise	91
7:27	Once, only once, and once for all	176
8:1	Rejoice, the Lord is King	194
9:5	As with gladness men of old	27
	Hail the day that sees him rise	91
	Once, only once, and once for all	176
9:11	Alleluia, sing to Jesus	7
10:19-20	Lord, the light of your love	141
11:1	Blessed assurance, Jesus is mine	37
11:3	Of the Father's love begotten	165
13:6	Abide with me	2
13:12	There is a green hill far away	219
13:15	All my hope on God is founded	13
	For the beauty of the earth	76

JAMES

1:17	Abide with me	2
	All my hope on God is founded	13
	Be still, my soul	33
	Fight the good fight	72
	Great is thy faithfulness	89
	Immortal, invisible, God only wise	109
	O strength and stay	182
	We plough the fields and scatter	241

1 PETER

1:6	What a friend we have in Jesus	243
1:10	All hail the power of Jesus' name	10
1:18-19	Blessed assurance, Jesus is mine	37
	The Church's one foundation	212
	There is a green hill far away	219
1:19	Bind us together, Lord	36
1:21	All my hope on God is founded	13
1:25	Lord, thy word abideth	142
2:4-6	Christ is made the sure foundation	44
	Christ is our cornerstone	45
2:21-22	All creatures of our God and King	4
	All hail the power of Jesus' name	10
2:24	Bread of heaven, on thee we feed	39
	The strife is o'er, the battle done	222
2:25	O Jesus, I have promised	170
3:18-19	Christ the Lord is risen again	46
5:7	All creatures of our God and King	6

2 PETER

| 3:8 | O God, our help in ages past | 168 |

1 JOHN

1:1	We love the place, O God	240
1:5	Lead, kindly light	130
1:7	The Spirit lives to set us free	221
2:1	And now, O Father, mindful of the love	21
2:16	Be thou my guardian and my guide	34
2:20	Come, Holy Ghost, our souls inspire	52
3:1	How deep the Father's love for us	101
3:2	How sweet the name of Jesus sounds	104
	Once in royal David's city	175
3:5	Be still, for the presence of the Lord	32
4:9	From heaven you came	78
4:12-13	Abide with me	2
4:16	God is love: his the care	83

REVELATION

1:5-6	Alleluia, sing to Jesus	7
1:7	Lo, he comes with clouds descending	136
1:8	Of the Father's love begotten	165
	Unto us a boy is born	237
	Love divine, all loves excelling	143
1:17-18	Rejoice, the Lord is King	194
2:4	Thy kingdom come, O God	232

2:10	For all the saints	75	7:14-15	Blessed assurance, Jesus is mine	37
3:7	O come, O come, Emmanuel	161	7:17	All heaven declares	11
4:6	Alleluia, sing to Jesus	7		Be still, my soul	33
4:6-9	Angel-voices ever singing	24	11:15	Crown him with many crowns	60
4:8	In the bleak midwinter	112	14:6	We have a gospel to proclaim	239
4:8-11	Awake, my soul, and with the sun	30	14:13	For all the saints	75
	Holy, holy, holy! Lord God almighty	99	15:4	Angels from the realms of glory	23
4:10	Love divine, all loves excelling	143	17:14	Alleluia, sing to Jesus	7
5:5	Hail the day that sees him rise	91	19:6-9	Come, ye thankful people come	59
	Ye choirs of new Jerusalem	249		The Church's one foundation	212
5:5-6	Alleluia, sing to Jesus	7	19:9	At the Lamb's high feast we sing	28
5:6	Christ the Lord is risen again	46	19:16	Alleluia, sing to Jesus	7
	O for a closer walk with God	163		Christ the Lord is risen again	46
5:6-14	Crown him with many crowns	60		Hosanna, hosanna	100
5:8-10	All hail the power of Jesus' name	10		Majesty, worship his majesty	146
	All heaven declares	11		The head that once was crowned with thorns	216
5:9	Alleluia, sing to Jesus	7	20:10	Ye choirs of new Jerusalem	249
	Lift high the cross	134	20:14	Guide me, O thou great Redeemer	90
	There is a green hill far away	219	21:1-2	In the bleak midwinter	112
5:11-14	I cannot tell	106	21:1-27	Light's abode, celestial Salem	135
	Majesty, worship his majesty	146	21:10	City of God, how broad and far	49
	Ye servants of God	251	21:2	The Church's one foundation	212
5:12	Come, let us join our cheerful songs	53		Ye choirs of new Jerusalem	249
	Come, ye faithful, raise the anthem	57	21:21	For all the saints	75
	Glorious things of thee are spoken	81	21:3-10	As with gladness men of old	27
	We have a gospel to proclaim	239	21:3-5	Be still, my soul	33
5:12-13	Hail the day that sees him rise	91	21:4	Oft in danger, oft in woe	166
5:13	All heaven declares	11		Thy kingdom come, O God	232
	Angel-voices ever singing	24	21:5	Hills of the north, rejoice	282
5:14	Praise to the Lord, the Almighty	191	22:1-3	Crown him with many crowns	60
6:9-10	All hail the power of Jesus' name	10		To thee, O Lord, our hearts we raise	235
	Angels from the realms of glory	23	22:1-4	All heaven declares	11
7:3	Lift high the cross	134		Guide me, O thou great Redeemer	90
7:9-17	Jerusalem the golden	117	22:13	Love divine, all loves excelling	143
7:10	Ye servants of God	251		Of the Father's love begotten	165
7:14	As we are gathered	26	22:16	Christ, whose glory fills the skies	48
	At the Lamb's high feast we sing	28		O come, O come, Emmanuel	161
	Blessed assurance, Jesus is mine	37	22:23	As with gladness men of old	27

Index of Uses

THE GOSPEL

Grace and Providence

All my hope on God is founded 13
Amazing grace 18
And can it be 19
Be still, for the presence
of the Lord 32
Breathe on me, Breath of God 40
Christ is made the
sure foundation 44
Christ is our cornerstone 45
Come down, O Love divine 51
Come, Holy Ghost,
our souls inspire 52
Come, thou Holy Spirit, come 55
Disposer supreme 63
Do not be afraid 64
Faithful Shepherd, feed me 66
Fight the good fight 72
Glorious things of
thee are spoken 81
God be in my head 82
God is love: his the care 83
God moves in a mysterious way 84
God of mercy, God of grace 85
Great is thy faithfulness 89
How firm a foundation 102
I am a new creation 105
I heard the voice of Jesus say 108
Immortal love, for ever full 110
It is a thing most wonderful 115
Jesus, good above all other 122
Lead us, heavenly Father, lead us 131
Let us, with a gladsome mind 133
Lord Jesus Christ 138
Lord Jesus, think on me 139
Lord of all hopefulness 140
Lord, the light of your love 141
Love divine, all loves excelling 143
Meekness and majesty 149
Morning has broken 150
New every morning is the love 156
O dearest Lord, thy sacred head 162
One more step along the
world I go 178
O thou who camest from above 183
Peace, perfect peace, is the gift 186
Put thou thy trust in God 192
Rock of ages 196
Soldiers of Christ, arise 201
Such love 206
The King of love my shepherd is 217
The Lord's my shepherd 218
Thou, whose almighty word 228
Thy hand, O God, has guided 231
What a friend we have in Jesus 243
When all thy mercies,
O my God 244
Will your anchor hold 248

Joy, Praise and Thanksgiving

All creatures of our God and King 4
All hail the power of Jesus' name 10
All heaven declares 11
All people that on earth do dwell 15
Angel-voices ever singing 24
At the name of Jesus 29
Blessed assurance, Jesus is mine 37
Bright the vision that delighted 42
Christ triumphant 47
Come, let us join our
cheerful songs 53

Come on and celebrate 54
Come, ye faithful,
raise the anthem 57
Crown him with many crowns 60
Father, we love you 71
Fill your hearts with joy
and gladness 73
For the beauty of the earth 76
Give me joy in my heart 79
Give thanks with a grateful heart 80
Glorious things of thee
are spoken 81
God of mercy, God of grace 85
Great is thy faithfulness 89
Hail to the Lord's anointed 92
Hallelujah, my Father 93
Hills of the north, rejoice 282
Holy, holy, holy! Lord
God almighty 99
Hosanna, hosanna 100
How sweet the name of
Jesus sounds 104
I danced in the morning 107
Immortal, invisible,
God only wise 109
I will enter his gates 116
Jesus is Lord 123
Jesus shall reign where'er the sun 125
Jesu, the very thought of thee 126
Jubilate, everybody 127
King of glory, King of peace 129
Let all the world in every
corner sing 132
Let us, with a gladsome mind 133
Lift high the cross 134
Light's abode, celestial Salem 135
Lord, for the years 137
Majesty, worship his majesty 146
Meekness and majesty 149
Morning has broken 150
My Jesus, my Saviour 153
Now thank we all our God 157
O for a thousand
tongues to sing 164
O God beyond all praising 167
O Lord, my God 172
On this day, the first of days 179
O praise ye the Lord! 180
O worship the King 184
O worship the Lord in
the beauty of holiness 185
Praise him, praise him,
praise him in the morning 187
Praise, my soul, the King
of heaven 188
Praise the Lord, ye heavens
adore him 189
Praise to the Holiest 190
Praise to the Lord, the Almighty 191
Rejoice, the Lord is King 194
Songs of thankfulness and praise 202
Stand up and bless the Lord 204
Tell out, my soul 210
There is a Redeemer 220
This is the day 225
Through all the changing
scenes of life 229
To God be the glory! 234
To the name of our salvation 236
When all thy mercies,
O my God 244
Ye holy angels bright 250
Ye servants of God 251
You shall go out with joy 253

Faith, Trust and Commitment

All for Jesus! 8
All my hope on God is founded 13
And did those feet in ancient time 20
A new commandment 22
Awake, my soul, and with the sun 30
Be still, my soul 33
Be thou my guardian and
my guide 34
Blest are the pure in heart 38
Father, hear the prayer we offer 67
Father, I place into your hands 68
Fight the good fight 72
Firmly I believe and truly 74
For all the saints 75
God's Spirit is in my heart 86
He who would valiant be 97
In heavenly love abiding 111
I, the Lord of sea and sky 114
Jesus calls: us o'er the tumult 96
Jesus, good above all other 122
Just as I am, without one plea 128
Lead, kindly light 130
Lift high the cross 134
Lord, for the years 137
Lord Jesus Christ 138
Lord of all hopefulness 140
Make me a channel
of your peace 147
Nearer, my God, to thee 155
O happy band of pilgrims 169
O Jesus, I have promised 170
One more step along the
world I go 178
Peace, perfect peace, is the gift 186
Put thou thy trust in God 192
Soldiers of Christ, arise 201
Stand up, stand up for Jesus 205
Take up thy cross, the
Saviour said 208
The King of love my shepherd is 217
The Lord's my shepherd 218
Through the night of
doubt and sorrow 230
Thy hand, O God, has guided 231
Will your anchor hold 248
Ye servants of the Lord 252

Temptation, Penitence and Forgiveness

All ye who seek a comfort sure 17
Be thou my guardian and
my guide 34
Dear Lord and Father
of mankind 61
Father of heaven,
whose love profound 69
Just as I am, without one plea 128
Lord Jesus, think on me 139
Will your anchor hold 248

Hope and Consolation

Abide with me 2
Alleluia, sing to Jesus 7
All my hope on God is founded 13
All ye who seek a comfort sure 17
Amazing grace 18
Be still, my soul 33
Blessed assurance, Jesus is mine 37
Blest are the pure in heart 38
Do not be afraid 64

God our strength and refuge 219
How lovely on the mountains 103
I cannot tell 106
Immortal love, for ever full 110
Light's abode, celestial Salem 135
O happy band of pilgrims 169
O Love, that wilt not let me go 173
Peace, perfect peace, is the gift 186
The Church's one foundation 212
Through the night of doubt
and sorrow 230
Thy kingdom come, O God 232
To be in your presence 233
To the name of our salvation 236

Healing

Immortal love, for ever full 110
To be in your presence 233

Suffering and Sorrow

All ye who seek a comfort sure 17
Be still, for the presence
of the Lord 32
Be still, my soul 33
Do not be afraid 64
Father, I place into your hands 68
How firm a foundation 102
How sweet the name of
Jesus sounds 104
Immortal love, for ever full 110
Peace, perfect peace, is the gift 186

Protection

Abide with me 2
All my hope on God is founded 13
Amazing grace 18
Be thou my guardian and
my guide 34
Do not be afraid 64
Eternal Father, strong to save 65
Jesu, lover of my soul 118
Lord Jesus, think on me 139
Loving Shepherd of thy sheep 145
O God, our help in ages past 168
Rock of ages 196
Thine for ever! God of love 224
Through all the changing
scenes of life 229
To be in your presence 233
Will your anchor hold 248

Redemption and Salvation

Alleluia, alleluia, hearts to
heaven and voices raise 6
Alleluia, sing to Jesus 7
Amazing grace 18
And can it be 19
At the name of Jesus 29
Be still, my soul 33
Blessed assurance, Jesus is mine 37
Christ triumphant 47
Crown him with many crowns 60
Disposer supreme 63
Do not be afraid 64
From heaven you came 78
Hallelujah, my Father 93
Hills of the north, rejoice 98
How lovely on the mountains 103
I am a new creation 105
I cannot tell 106

I danced in the morning 107
Lift high the cross 134
Light's abode, celestial Salem 135
Meekness and majesty 149
Nearer, my God, to thee 155
Rock of ages 196
The Church's one foundation 212
There is a Redeemer 220
To God be the glory 234
To the name of our salvation 236

The Journey of Life
(*Hymns which, being singular, do not fit under The Pilgrim Community*)

Amazing grace 18
Be thou my guardian
    and my guide 34
Faithful Shepherd, feed me 66
Guide me, O thou
    great Redeemer 90
Lead, kindly light 130
Nearer, my God, to thee 155
O for a closer walk with God 163
One more step along the
    world I go 178
Put thou thy trust in God 192

THE CHURCH THE PEOPLE OF GOD

The Communion of Saints

All hail the power of Jesus' name 10
And now, O Father, mindful
    of the love 21
Angel-voices ever singing 24
Christ is our cornerstone 45
Come, let us join our
    cheerful songs 53
Disposer supreme 63
For all the saints 75
Holy, holy, holy!
    Lord God almighty 99
Jerusalem the golden 117
Light's abode, celestial Salem 135
O God, our help in ages past 168
The Church's one foundation 212
Ye holy angels bright 250

The Body of Christ

A new commandment 22
As we are gathered 26
Bind us together, Lord 36

The Serving Community

From heaven you came 78
Love divine, all loves excelling 143
My Jesus, my Saviour 153
Ye servants of the Lord 252

The Witnessing Community

All for Jesus! 8
Colours of day 50
Come, let us join our
    cheerful songs 53
Disposer supreme 63
Firmly I believe and truly 74
For all the saints 75
God's Spirit is in my heart 86
Jesus calls us: o'er the tumult 119
O Breath of Life 159
We have a gospel to proclaim 239

The Suffering Community

From heaven you came 78

The Pilgrim Community

Be thou my guardian and
    my guide 34
Do not be afraid 64
Father, hear the prayer we offer 67
Lead us, heavenly Father, lead us 131
Oft in danger, oft in woe 166
O happy band of pilgrims 169
The Spirit lives to set us free 221
Through the night of
    doubt and sorrow 230
Thy hand, O God, has guided 231

Christian Unity

As we are gathered 26
Bind us together, Lord 36
Bright the vision that delighted 42
Christ is made the
    sure foundation 44
City of God, how broad and far 49
Come, Holy Ghost,
    our souls inspire 52
Love divine, all loves excelling 143
Through the night of doubt
    and sorrow 230
Thy hand, O God, has guided 231

THE WORLD

The Nation

And did those feet in
    ancient time 20
Lord, for the years 137
Rejoice, O land, in God
    thy might 193

The Wholeness of Creation

All creatures of our God and King 4
All things bright and beautiful 16
Dear Lord and Father
    of mankind 61

Human Rights

God's Spirit is in my heart 86
Stand up, stand up for Jesus 205

Aid and Development

I, the Lord of sea and sky 114

Evangelism

All for Jesus! 8
All over the world 14
And did those feet in ancient time 20
At the name of Jesus 29
Colours of day 50
God's Spirit is in my heart 86
Go forth and tell 87
How lovely on the mountains 103
I, the Lord of sea and sky 114
Jesus calls: us o'er the tumult 119
Jesus, good above all other 122
Jesus shall reign where'er the sun 125
Lift high the cross 134
Lord, for the years 137
Lord, the light of your love 141
Make way, make way 148
O Breath of Life 159
Stand up, stand up for Jesus 205
Thou, whose almighty word 228
Thy kingdom come, O God 232
We are marching 238
We have a gospel to proclaim 239

TIMES AND SEASONS

Hymns generally applicable to the main seasons are included here. For suggestions more specifically related to the Lectionary, see the Common Worship Lectionary Index.

Morning

All creatures of our God and King 4
Awake, my soul, and with the sun 30
Christ, whose glory fills the skies 48
Colours of day 50
Give me joy in my heart 79
Jesus shall reign where'er the sun 125
Lord, the light of your love 141
Morning has broken 150
New every morning is the love 156
When all thy mercies,
    O my God 244

Evening

Abide with me 2
Lead, kindly light 130
O strength and stay 182
Saviour, again to thy dear
    name we raise 197
Sun of my soul, thou
    Saviour dear 207
The day thou gavest, Lord,
    is ended 214

Advent

Be still, for the presence
    of the Lord 32
Come, thou long-expected Jesus 56
Hail to the Lord's anointed 92
Hark! a herald voice is calling 94
Hark, the glad sound 95
Hills of the north, rejoice 98
How lovely on the mountains 103
Lo, he comes with clouds
    descending 136
Love divine, all loves excelling 143
Make way, make way 148
O come, O come, Emmanuel 161
Tell out, my soul 210
Thou didst leave thy throne 227
Thy kingdom come, O God 232
Waken, O sleeper, wake and rise 702
Ye servants of the Lord 252

Christmas

A great and mighty wonder 3
Angels from the realms of glory 23
Christians, awake! 43
Ding dong! merrily on high 62
Good King Wenceslas 88
Hark, the herald-angels sing 96
In the bleak mid-winter 112
Lord Jesus Christ 138
O come, all ye faithful 160
Of the Father's love begotten 165
O little one sweet,
    O little one mild 507
O little town of Bethlehem 171
Once in royal David's city 175
On Christmas night,
    all Christians sing 177
See, amid the winter's snow 198
See him lying on a bed of straw 199
The angel Gabriel from
    heaven came 211
The first Nowell 215

Thou didst leave thy throne 227
Unto us a boy is born 237
While shepherds watched 744

Christmas
Children's Hymns and Songs

Away in a manger 31

New Year and Anniversaries

A new commandment 22
Be thou my guardian
    and my guide 34
Be thou my vision 35
Breathe on me, Breath of God 40
Lord, for the years 137

Epiphany

As with gladness men of old 27
Brightest and best 41
God of mercy, God of grace 85
Hail to the Lord's anointed 92
Hills of the north, rejoice 98
Jesus shall reign 125
Thou whose almighty word 514
Lord, the light of your love 141
O worship the Lord in the
    beauty of holiness 185
Songs of thankfulness and praise 202
We three kings of Orient are 242

Lent

Be still, for the presence
    of the Lord 32
Be thou my guardian
    and my guide 34
Dear Lord and Father
    of mankind 61
Father, hear the prayer we offer 67
Forty days and forty nights 77
Just as I am, without one plea 128
Lord Jesus, think on me 139
Oft in danger, oft in woe 166
Praise to the Holiest 190
Put thou thy trust in God 192
Rock of ages 196
Take up thy cross,
    the Saviour said 208
Will your anchor hold 248

Passiontide

All glory, laud and honour 9
All ye who seek a comfort sure 17
From heaven you came 78
Immortal love, for ever full 110
It is a thing most wonderful 115
Lift high the Cross 134
My God, I love thee 152
My song is love unknown 154
O dearest Lord, thy sacred head 162
On a hill far away 174
Once, only once, and once for all 176
O sacred head sore wounded 181
Praise to the Holiest 190
Ride on, ride on in majesty 195
Rock of ages 196
There is a green hill far away 219
When I survey the
    wondrous cross 246

Easter

Alleluia, alleluia, give thanks
    to the risen Lord 5

Alleluia, alleluia, hearts to
   heaven and voices raise   6
Alleluia, sing to Jesus   7
All heaven declares   11
At the Lamb's high feast we sing   28
Christ the Lord is risen again   46
Colours of day   50
Come, ye faithful,
   raise the anthem   57
Come, ye faithful,
   raise the strain   58
I danced in the morning   107
I know that my Redeemer lives   311
Jesus Christ is risen today   121
Jesus is Lord   123
Jesus lives! thy terrors now   124
Light's abode, celestial Salem   135
Love's redeeming work is done   144
Morning has broken   150
Now the green blade riseth   158
The day of resurrection   213
The strife is o'er, the battle done   222
Thine be the glory   223
This joyful Eastertide   226
Ye choirs of new Jerusalem   249

Ascensiontide

All hail the power of Jesus' name   10
All heaven declares   11
At the name of Jesus   29
Christ triumphant   47
Come, let us join our
   cheerful songs   53
Come, ye faithful, raise
   the anthem   57
Crown him with many crowns   60
Hail the day that sees him rise   91
Hail to the Lord's anointed   92
Jesus shall reign   125
Majesty, worship his majesty   146
Rejoice, the Lord is King   194
Stand up, stand up for Jesus   205
The head that once was
   crowned with thorns   216
Thine be the glory   223
Ye servants of God   251

Pentecost

Breathe on me, Breath of God   40
Come down, O Love divine   51
Come, Holy Ghost, our
   souls inspire   52
Come, thou Holy Spirit, come   55
God's Spirit is in my heart   86
Go forth and tell   87
O thou who camest from above   183
Spirit of the living God (Iverson)   203
The Spirit lives to set us free   221

The Holy Trinity

Come, Holy Ghost,
   our souls inspire   52
Father of heaven,
   whose love profound   69
Firmly I believe and truly   74

Holy, holy, holy!
   Lord God almighty   99
Thou, whose almighty word   228

Harvest Festival

All creatures of our God and King   4
Angel-voices ever singing   24
Come, ye thankful people, come   59
Fill your hearts with joy
   and gladness   73
For the beauty of the earth   76
Let us, with a gladsome mind   133
To thee, O Lord, our hearts
   we raise   235
We plough the fields and scatter   241

All Saints

All hail the power of Jesus' name   10
All heaven declares   11
Bind us together, Lord   36
Christ is our cornerstone   45
Disposer supreme   63
For all the saints   75
Jerusalem the golden   117
Light's abode, celestial Salem   135
Thy hand, O God, has guided   231
Ye holy angels bright   250

Remembrance

Eternal Father, strong to save   65
O God, our help in ages past   168

Patronal Festivals

Praise the Lord, ye heavens
   adore him   189

THE SACRAMENTS

Baptism

Alleluia, alleluia, hearts to
   heaven and voices raise   6
Come, ye faithful,
   raise the strain   58
Do not be afraid   64
Firmly I believe and truly   74
For all the saints   75
Jesus calls us: o'er the tumult   119
Loving Shepherd of thy sheep   145
Morning has broken   150
The Church's one foundation   212

Confirmation

Amazing grace   18
Be still, for the presence
   of the Lord   32
Be thou my guardian and
   my guide   34
Be thou my vision   35
Breathe on me, Breath of God   40
Christ is our cornerstone   45
Come down, O Love divine   51
Come, Holy Ghost,
   our souls inspire   52
Father, hear the prayer we offer   67

Firmly I believe and truly   74
For all the saints   75
Glorious things of thee
   are spoken   81
God's Spirit is in my heart   86
Lord, the light of your love   141
O Breath of Life   159
O Jesus, I have promised   170
One more step along the
   world I go   178
O thou who camest from above   183
Spirit of the living God (Iverson)   203
Stand up, stand up for Jesus   205

Holy Communion

Alleluia, sing to Jesus   7
All for Jesus!   8
And now, O Father,
   mindful of the love   21
At the Lamb's high feast we sing   28
Be still, for the presence
   of the Lord   32
Bread of heaven, on thee we feed   39
Lord Jesus Christ   138
My God, and is thy table spread   151
Once, only once,
   and once for all   176

Marriage

A new commandment   22
Lead us, heavenly Father, lead us   131
Lord, for the years   137
Lord of all hopefulness   140
Love divine, all loves excelling   143

Funerals
(See also The Communion of Saints)

Abide with me   2
As with gladness men of old   27
Immortal, love for ever full   243
In heavenly love abiding   111
Jerusalem the golden   117
O Love, that wilt not let me go   173
Rock of ages   196
The day thou gavest, Lord,
   is ended   214

Ordination/Commissioning
(See also Baptism and
Confirmation)

Firmly I believe and truly   74
Lord, for the years   137
O thou who camest from above   183
Ye servants of the Lord   252

THE ORDER FOR
HOLY COMMUNION

Opening Hymn

All creatures of our God and King   4
All people that on earth
   do dwell   15
Angel-voices ever singing   24
As we are gathered   26

Awake, my soul, and
   with the sun   30
Come, let us join our
   cheerful songs   53
Come on and celebrate   54
Come, ye faithful,
   raise the anthem   57
God of mercy, God of grace   85
I will enter his gates   116
Jubilate, everybody   127
Let us, with a gladsome mind   133
Lord, the light of your love   141
Morning has broken   150
O Breath of Life   159
O God beyond all praising   167
O worship the King   184
O worship the Lord in
   the beauty of holiness   185
Stand up and bless the Lord   204
This is the day   225
To God be the glory!   234
To the name of our salvation   236
Ye holy angels bright   250
Ye servants of God   251

Gradual Hymn

Dear Lord and Father
   of mankind   61
Lord, for the years   137
Lord, the light of your love   141
Lord, thy word abideth   142
Tell out, my soul   210
Thou, whose almighty word   228
Thy hand, O God, has guided   231

Offertory Hymn

Abba, Father, let me be   1
Angel-voices ever singing   24
For the beauty of the earth   76
O worship the Lord in the
   beauty of holiness   185

Communion

And now, O Father, mindful
   of the love   21
As we are gathered   26
Be still, for the presence of
   the Lord   32
Bread of heaven, on thee we feed   39
Come, Holy Ghost,
   our souls inspire   52
Peace, perfect peace, is the gift   186

Final Hymn

God's Spirit is in my heart   86
Go forth and tell   87
Lead us, heavenly Father,
   lead us   131
Saviour, again to thy dear
   name we raise   197
The angel Gabriel from
   heaven came   211
You shall go out with joy   253

Index of Hymns for the Common Worship Lectionary

YEAR A

ADVENT

FIRST SUNDAY OF ADVENT - A

Come, thou long expected Jesus 56
Ye servants of the Lord 252

SECOND SUNDAY OF ADVENT - A

Crown him with many crowns 60
Hail to the Lord's anointed 92
Jesus shall reign where'er the sun 125
O come, O come, Emmanuel 161

THIRD SUNDAY OF ADVENT - A

Tell out, my soul 210
The angel Gabriel from
   heaven came 211

FOURTH SUNDAY OF ADVENT - A

O come, O come, Emmanuel 161
The angel Gabriel from
   heaven came 211

CHRISTMAS

CHRISTMAS EVE - FOR YEARS A, B and C
Any of the following Sets may be used on the evening of Christmas Eve

CHRISTMAS DAY - FOR YEARS A, B and C

Set I

A great and mighty wonder 3
Angels from the realms of glory 23
Brightest and best 41
Christians, awake! 43
Crown him with many crowns 60
Ding dong! merrily on high 62
Hark, the herald angels sing 96
I cannot tell 106
In the bleak midwinter 112
It came upon the midnight clear 113
Jesus, good above all other 122
O come, all ye faithful 160
O little town of Bethlehem 171
Once in royal David's city 175
On Christmas night
   all Christians sing 177
See amid the winter's snow 198
See him lying on a bed of straw 199
The first Nowell 215
Thou didst leave thy throne 227
Unto us a boy is born 237
We have a gospel to proclaim 239
When our God came to earth 740
While shepherds watched 247
Children's Hymns and Songs
Away in a manger 31

Set II

A great and mighty wonder 3
Angels from the realms of glory 23

Brightest and best 41
Christians, awake! 43
Ding dong! merrily on high 62
Hark, the herald angels sing 96
I cannot tell 106
In the bleak midwinter 112
It came upon the midnight clear 113
Jesus, good above all other 122
O come, all ye faithful 160
O little town of Bethlehem 171
On Christmas night
   all Christians sing 177
Once in royal David's city 175
See amid the winter's snow 198
See him lying on a bed of straw 199
The first Nowell 215
Thou didst leave thy throne 227
Unto us a boy is born 237
While shepherds watched 247
Children's Hymns and Songs
Away in a manger 31

Set III

A great and mighty wonder 3
At the name of Jesus 29
Christians, awake! 43
Hark, the herald angels sing 96
How lovely on the mountains 103
O come, all ye faithful 160
Of the Father's love begotten 165
We have a gospel to proclaim 239

FIRST SUNDAY OF CHRISTMAS - A

O praise ye the Lord 180
Praise, my soul,
   the King of heaven 188
Praise the Lord,
   ye heavens adore him 189
Unto us a boy is born 237
Ye holy angels bright 250

SECOND SUNDAY OF CHRISTMAS - FOR YEARS A, B and C

A great and mighty wonder 3
At the name of Jesus 29
Breathe on me, Breath of God 40
Christ triumphant 47
Come, ye faithful, raise
   the anthem 57
Crown him with many crowns 60
Father of heaven, whose
   love profound 69
Fill your hearts with joy
   and gladness 73
Lord, the light of your love 141
Of the Father's love begotten 165
We have a gospel to proclaim 239

EPIPHANY

THE EPIPHANY - FOR YEARS A, B and C

A great and mighty wonder 3
As with gladness men of old 27
Blessed assurance, Jesus is mine 37
Brightest and best 41
Hail to the Lord's anointed 92
Jesus shall reign where'er the sun 125

Brightest and best 41
Christians, awake! 43
Ding dong! merrily on high 62
Hark, the herald angels sing 96
I cannot tell 106
In the bleak midwinter 112
It came upon the midnight clear 113
Jesus, good above all other 122
O come, all ye faithful 160
O little town of Bethlehem 171
On Christmas night
   all Christians sing 177
Once in royal David's city 175
See amid the winter's snow 198
See him lying on a bed of straw 199
The first Nowell 215
Thou didst leave thy throne 227
Unto us a boy is born 237
While shepherds watched 247
Children's Hymns and Songs
Away in a manger 31

O worship the Lord in the
   beauty of holiness 185
We three kings of Orient are 242

THE BAPTISM OF CHRIST - A

How firm a foundation 102

SECOND SUNDAY OF EPIPHANY - A

And did those feet in ancient time 20
Just as I am, without one plea 128
There is a Redeemer 220

THIRD SUNDAY OF EPIPHANY - A

Dear Lord and Father
   of mankind 61
Jesus calls us: o'er the tumult 119
Put thou thy trust in God 192
Thy kingdom come, O God 232

FOURTH SUNDAY OF EPIPHANY - A

Disposer supreme 63
Immortal, invisible 109
Jesu, lover of my soul 118

THE PRESENTATION OF CHRIST IN THE TEMPLE - FOR YEARS A, B and C
Candlemass

King of glory, King of peace 129
Make way, make way 148

ORDINARY TIME

PROPER 1 - A

Lord, the light of your love 141

PROPER 2 - A

Be thou my vision 35
Bind us together, Lord 36

PROPER 3 - A

Christ is made the
   sure foundation 44

SECOND SUNDAY BEFORE LENT - A

All my hope on God is founded 13
Eternal Father, strong to save 65
Let us, with a gladsome mind 133
Lord, the light of your love 141
O Breath of Life 159
On this day, the first of days 179
Thou whose almighty word 228

SUNDAY NEXT BEFORE LENT - A

Thy kingdom come, O God 232

LENT

ASH WEDNESDAY - FOR YEARS A, B and C

Give thanks with a
   grateful heart 80

FIRST SUNDAY OF LENT - A

Forty days and forty nights 77
Lead us, heavenly Father, lead us 131

SECOND SUNDAY OF LENT - A

All my hope on God is founded 13
Christ triumphant, ever reigning 47
From heaven you came 78
I cannot tell 106
To God be the glory 234

THIRD SUNDAY OF LENT - A

Father, hear the prayer we offer 67
I am a new creation 105
I cannot tell 106
I heard the voice of Jesus say 108
Jesu, lover of my soul 118
Jesu, the very thought of thee 126
O Breath of Life 159

FOURTH SUNDAY OF LENT - A

Amazing grace 18
Faithful Shepherd, feed me 66
Father, hear the prayer we offer 67
In heavenly love abiding 111
The King of love my shepherd is 217
The Lord's my shepherd 218

Or: MOTHERING SUNDAY - FOR YEARS A, B and C

Bind us together, Lord 36

FIFTH SUNDAY OF LENT - A

Breathe on me, Breath of God 40
O Breath of Life 159
The Spirit lives to set us free 221

PALM SUNDAY - A

Liturgy of the Palms

All glory, laud and honour 9
Christ is made the
   sure foundation 44
Give me joy in my heart 79
Hosanna, hosanna 100
I will enter his gates 116
Ride on, ride on in majesty 195
This is the day, this is the day 225

Liturgy of the Passion

And can it be 19
From heaven you came 78
Meekness and majesty 149
My song is love unknown 154
O dearest Lord, thy sacred head 162
O sacred head sore wounded 181
Praise to the Holiest in
   the height 190
To the name of our salvation 236

MONDAY OF HOLY WEEK - FOR YEARS A, B and C

Father of heaven, whose
   love profound 69
How firm a foundation 102

Immortal, invisible	109		
Jesu, lover of my soul	118		

TUESDAY OF HOLY WEEK -
FOR YEARS A, B and C

Disposer supreme	63
Father, we love you	71
For all the saints	75
The Spirit lives to set us free	221

WEDNESDAY OF HOLY WEEK -
FOR YEARS A, B and C

Christ triumphant	47

MAUNDY THURSDAY -
FOR YEARS A, B and C

All my hope on God is founded	13
Amazing grace	18
A new commandment	22
Lord Jesus Christ	138
Meekness and majesty	149
Once, only once, and once for all	176
Peace, perfect peace, is the gift	186

GOOD FRIDAY -
FOR YEARS A, B and C

How sweet the name of Jesus sounds	104
Meekness and majesty	149
My song is love unknown	154
O dearest Lord, thy sacred head	162
O sacred head sore wounded	181
Praise to the Holiest in the height	190
Rock of ages, cleft for me	196
The head that once was crowned with thorns	216
There is a green hill far away	219
What a friend we have in Jesus	243

EASTER EVE -
FOR YEARS A, B and C

Services other than the Easter Vigil

For all the saints	75
Love's redeeming work is done	144
New every morning is the love	156

EASTER

EASTER VIGIL -
FOR YEARS A, B and C

All heaven declares	11
All my hope on God is founded	13
At the Lamb's high feast we sing	28
Be still, for the presence of the Lord	32
Breathe on me, Breath of God	40
Come, ye faithful, raise the strain	58
Glorious things of thee are spoken	81
I, the Lord of sea and sky	114
Let us, with a gladsome mind	133
Lord, the light of your love	141
My God, and is thy table spread	151
My Jesus, my Saviour	153
On this day, the first of days	179
Put thou thy trust in God	192
Thine be the glory	223
This joyful Eastertide	226

EASTER DAY - A

Christ is made the sure foundation	44
I will enter his gates	116
Love's redeeming work is done	144
On this day, the first of days	179
Thine be the glory	223
This is the day, this is the day	225

SECOND SUNDAY
OF EASTER - A

At the Lamb's high feast we sing	28
Be thou my vision	35
Come, ye faithful, raise the strain	58
Crown him with many crowns	60
Jerusalem the golden	117
Thine be the glory	223
This joyful Eastertide	226
To the name of our salvation	236
We have a gospel to proclaim	239
What a friend we have in Jesus	243

THIRD SUNDAY OF EASTER - A

All my hope on God is founded	13
Bind us together, Lord	36

FOURTH SUNDAY
OF EASTER - A

All creatures of our God and King	4
All hail the power of Jesus' name	10
Faithful Shepherd, feed me	66
Father, hear the prayer we offer	67
For all the saints	75
In heavenly love abiding	111
O Jesus, I have promised	170
The King of love my shepherd is	217
The Lord's my shepherd, I'll not want	218

FIFTH SUNDAY OF EASTER - A

Christ is made the sure foundation	44
Christ is our cornerstone	45
How sweet the name of Jesus sounds	104
Jesu, lover of my soul	118
O Jesus, I have promised	170
Thine for ever! God of love	224

SIXTH SUNDAY OF EASTER - A

Alleluia, sing to Jesus	7
Christ the Lord is risen again	46
Great is thy faithfulness	89

ASCENSION DAY -
FOR YEARS A, B and C

Alleluia, sing to Jesus	7
Angel voices, ever singing	24
At the name of Jesus	29
Come, let us join our cheerful songs	53
Come, ye faithful, raise the anthem	57
Crown him with many crowns	60
Hail the day that sees him rise	91
Immortal, invisible	109
My Jesus, my Saviour	153
O worship the King	184

SEVENTH SUNDAY
OF EASTER - A

Alleluia, sing to Jesus	7
At the name of Jesus	29
God moves in a mysterious way	84

PENTECOST (Whit Sunday) - A

Angel voices, ever singing	24
Bind us together, Lord	36
Breathe on me, Breath of God	40
Come down, O Love divine	51
Jesus is Lord	123
Lord, the light of your love	141
O Breath of Life	159
Thine be the glory	223

ORDINARY TIME

TRINITY SUNDAY - A

Alleluia, sing to Jesus	7
Be thou my guardian and my guide	34
Go forth and tell	87
Jesus shall reign where'er the sun	125
Loving Shepherd of thy sheep	145
O Lord, my God	172

DAY OF THANKSGIVING
FOR HOLY COMMUNION
Thursday after Trinity Sunday
(Corpus Christi)
FOR YEARS A, B and C

All my hope on God is founded	13
Amazing grace	18
Bread of heaven, on thee we feed	39
Lord Jesus Christ	138
Once, only once, and once for all	176

PROPER 4 - A

Be still, for the presence of the Lord	32
For all the saints	75
Glorious things of thee are spoken	81
Immortal love, for ever full	110
Jesus, lover of my soul	118
My Jesus, my Saviour	153
O God, our help in ages past	168

PROPER 5 - A

Immortal love, for ever full	110

PROPER 6 - A

All my hope on God is founded	13
All people that on earth do dwell	15
I am a new creation	105
I will enter his gates	116
Jubilate, everybody	127

PROPER 7 - A

Great is thy faithfulness	89
My Jesus, my Saviour	153
Praise, my soul, the King of heaven	188
Take up thy cross, the Saviour said	208

PROPER 8 - A

Amazing grace	18
O Lord, my God	172

PROPER 9 - A

Alleluia, sing to Jesus	7
All ye who seek a comfort sure	17
I cannot tell	106
I danced in the morning	107
I heard the voice of Jesus say	108
Love divine, all loves excelling	143
Praise, my soul, the King of heaven	188

PROPER 10 - A

And can it be	19
Come, ye faithful, raise the anthem	57
I am a new creation	105
The Spirit lives to set us free	221
You shall go out with joy	253

PROPER 11 - A

Abba, Father, let me be	1
Blessed assurance, Jesus is mine	37
Great is thy faithfulness	89
Nearer, my God, to thee	155
Praise, my soul, the King of heaven	188

PROPER 13 - A

Praise, my soul, the King of heaven	188
Put thou thy trust in God	192

PROPER 14 - A

Alleluia, alleluia, give thanks to the risen Lord	5
Dear Lord and Father of mankind	61
Eternal Father, strong to save	65
Fill your hearts with joy and gladness	73
Go forth and tell	87
We love the place, O God	240

PROPER 15 - A

God of mercy, God of grace	85

PROPER 16 - A

O God, our help in ages past	168

PROPER 17 - A

Be still, for the presence of the Lord	32
Take up thy cross, the Saviour said	208
The head that once was crowned with thorns	216
We love the place, O God	240

PROPER 18 - A

Come, ye faithful, raise the anthem	57
Lord, the light of your love	141

PROPER 19 - A

Great is thy faithfulness	89
Praise, my soul, the King of heaven	188

PROPER 20 - A

Father, hear the prayer we offer	67

Glorious things of thee
  are spoken 81
Guide me,
  O thou great Redeemer 90
My God, and is thy
  table spread 151
Praise, my soul,
  the King of heaven 188

PROPER 21 - A

And can it be 19
At the name of Jesus 29
Blest are the pure in heart 38
Christ triumphant, ever reigning 47
Father, hear the prayer we offer 67
For all the saints 75
Jesu, lover of my soul 118
Meekness and majesty 149
Praise to the Holiest
  in the height 190
To the name of our salvation 236

PROPER 22 - A

All heaven declares 11
And now, O Father,
  mindful of the love 21
As the deer pants for the water 25
Fight the good fight 72
Make way, make way 148

PROPER 23 - A

Father, hear the prayer we offer 67
Faithful Shepherd, feed me 66
In heavenly love abiding 111
The King of love my shepherd is 217
The Lord's my shepherd 218
Thy hand, O God, has guided 231

PROPER 24 - A

All my hope on God
  is founded 13
Rock of ages, cleft for me 196

PROPER 25 - A

Hail to the Lord's anointed 92
Love divine, all loves excelling 143
O God, our help in ages past 168

Or: BIBLE SUNDAY - A

Bind us together, Lord 36
Come down, O Love divine 51

DEDICATION FESTIVAL - A

City of God, how broad and far 49
Give me joy in my heart 79
Hosanna, hosanna 100
My song is love unknown 154

ALL SAINTS' DAY - A

All heaven declares 11
As we are gathered 26
At the Lamb's high feast we sing 28
Blessed assurance, Jesus is mine 37
Blest are the pure in heart 38
Fill your hearts with
  joy and gladness 73
How sweet the name
  of Jesus sounds 104
Jerusalem the golden 117
Make way, make way 148

The Church's one foundation 212
Through all the changing
  scenes of life 229
Ye servants of God 251

FOURTH SUNDAY
BEFORE ADVENT - A

All my hope on God is founded 13
O, Jesus I have promised 170
We have a gospel to proclaim 239

THIRD SUNDAY
BEFORE ADVENT - A

Give me joy in my heart 79

SECOND SUNDAY
BEFORE ADVENT - A

O God, our help in ages past 168

CHRIST THE KING - A

At the name of Jesus 29
For all the saints 75
Guide me,
  O thou great Redeemer 90
Of the Father's love begotten 165
When I needed a neighbour 245

YEAR B

ADVENT

FIRST SUNDAY OF ADVENT - B

Hark! a herald voice is calling 94
Lo, he comes with
  clouds descending 136

SECOND SUNDAY
OF ADVENT - B

Fill your hearts with joy
  and gladness 73
I cannot tell 106
Immortal, invisible 109
Lord, thy word abideth 142
O God, our help in ages past 168
Praise, my soul,
  the King of heaven 188

THIRD SUNDAY
OF ADVENT - B

Hail to the Lord's anointed 92
Hark the glad sound!
  the Saviour comes 95
I cannot tell 106
Make way, make way 148
O for a thousand tongues to sing 164
Tell out, my soul 210

FOURTH SUNDAY
OF ADVENT - B

Crown him with many crowns 60
Rejoice, the Lord is King 194
Tell out, my soul 210
The angel Gabriel from
  heaven came 211

CHRISTMAS

CHRISTMAS EVE - See Year A

CHRISTMAS DAY - See Year A

FIRST SUNDAY
OF CHRISTMAS - B

Abba, Father, let me be 1
Angel voices ever singing 24
O praise ye the Lord 180
Praise, my soul,
  the King of heaven 188
Praise the Lord,
  ye heavens adore him 189
Ye holy angels bright 250

SECOND SUNDAY
OF CHRISTMAS - See Year A

EPIPHANY

THE EPIPHANY - See YEAR A

THE BAPTISM OF CHRIST - B

Eternal Father, strong to save 65
Lord of our life 417
Lord, the light of your love 141
O Breath of Life 159
On this day, the first of days 179
Thou, whose almighty word 228

SECOND SUNDAY
OF EPIPHANY - B

All hail the power of Jesus' name 10
O for a closer walk with God 163

THIRD SUNDAY
OF EPIPHANY - B

At the Lamb's high feast we sing 28
Come, ye thankful people, come 59
The Church's one foundation 212

FOURTH SUNDAY
OF EPIPHANY - B

Give thanks with a
  grateful heart 80
There is a Redeemer 220

THE PRESENTATION OF
CHRIST IN THE TEMPLE -
See YEAR A

ORDINARY TIME

PROPER 1 - B

Fill your hearts with joy
  and gladness 73
We have a gospel to proclaim 239

PROPER 2 - B

Fight the good fight 72

PROPER 3 - B

Dear Lord and Father
  of mankind 61

SECOND SUNDAY
BEFORE LENT - B

Angel voices, ever singing 24
At the name of Jesus 29
Breathe on me, Breath of God 40
Christ triumphant 47
Crown him with many crowns 60
Father of heaven,
  whose love profound 69

My song is love unknown 154
We have a gospel to proclaim 239

SUNDAY NEXT
BEFORE LENT - B

Be still, for the presence
  of the Lord 32
Christ whose glory fills the skies 48
Lord, the light of your love 141

LENT

ASH WEDNESDAY - See YEAR A

FIRST SUNDAY OF LENT - B

Forty days and forty nights 77
Jesu, lover of my soul 118
Lead us, heavenly Father,
  lead us 131

SECOND SUNDAY OF LENT - B

At the name of Jesus 29
Take up thy cross,
  the Saviour said 208

THIRD SUNDAY OF LENT - B

All heaven declares 11
As the deer pants for the water 25

FOURTH SUNDAY OF LENT - B

From heaven you came 78
To God be the glory 234

Or: MOTHERING SUNDAY -
See YEAR A

FIFTH SUNDAY OF LENT - B

Father, we love you 71

PALM SUNDAY - B

Liturgy of the Palms

All glory, laud and honour 9
Christ is made the
  sure foundation 44
Give my joy in my heart 79
Hosanna, hosanna 100
I will enter his gates 116
My song is love unknown 154
Ride on, ride on in majesty 195
This is the day 225

Liturgy of the Passion

And can it be 19
At the name of Jesus 29
Be thou my guardian
  and my guide 34
Blest are the pure in heart 38
Christ triumphant,
  ever reigning 47
For all the saints 75
From heaven you came 78
Meekness and majesty 149
My song is love unknown 154
O dearest Lord, thy sacred head 162
O sacred head sore wounded 181
Praise to the Holiest 190
To the name of our salvation 236

MONDAY OF HOLY WEEK -
See YEAR A

TUESDAY OF HOLY WEEK -
See YEAR A

WEDNESDAY OF HOLY WEEK -
See YEAR A

MAUNDY THURSDAY -
See YEAR A

GOOD FRIDAY - See YEAR A

EASTER EVE - See YEAR A
Services other than the Easter Vigil

EASTER

EASTER VIGIL - See YEAR A

EASTER DAY - B

A new commandment 22
Christ is made the
    sure foundation 44
I will enter his gates 116
Love's redeeming work is done 144
Now the green blade riseth 158
On this day, the first of days 179
Thine be the glory 223
This is the day 225

SECOND SUNDAY
OF EASTER - B

And now, O Father,
    mindful of the love 21
Blessed assurance, Jesus is mine 37
Crown him with many crowns 60
Saviour, again to thy dear
    name we raise 197
The Spirit lives to set us free 221
Thine be the glory 223
We love the place, O God 240

THIRD SUNDAY OF EASTER - B

How sweet the name of
    Jesus sounds 104
Thine be the glory 223

FOURTH SUNDAY
OF EASTER - B

All for Jesus! 8
All hail the power of Jesus' name 10
Christ is made the
    sure foundation 44
Faithful Shepherd, feed me 66
Father, hear the prayer we offer 67
How sweet the name of
    Jesus sounds 104
I cannot tell 106
In heavenly love abiding 111
Loving shepherd of thy sheep 145
The King of love my shepherd is 217
The Lord's my shepherd 218
Thine for ever! God of love 224
To the name of our salvation 236

FIFTH SUNDAY OF EASTER - B

God is love: his the care 83
I danced in the morning 107

SIXTH SUNDAY OF EASTER - B

Put thou thy trust in God 192

ASCENSION DAY - see YEAR A

SEVENTH SUNDAY
OF EASTER - B

I, the Lord of sea and sky 114

PENTECOST (Whit Sunday) - B

Angel voices, ever singing 24
Breathe on me, Breath of God 40
Come down, O Love divine 51
Come, Holy Ghost,
    our souls inspire 52
Lord, the light of your love 141
O Breath of Life 159
On this day, the first of days 179

ORDINARY TIME

TRINITY SUNDAY - B

Abba, Father, let me be 1
Bright the vision
    that delighted 42
From heaven you came 78
Hallelujah, my Father 93
I cannot tell 106
Immortal, invisible 109
I, the Lord of sea and sky 114
Lord, the light of your love 141
To God be the glory 234

DAY OF THANKSGIVING FOR
HOLY COMMUNION
Thursday After Trinity Sunday
(Corpus Christi) See YEAR A

PROPER 4 - B

Disposer supreme 63
Lord, the light of your love 141

PROPER 5 - B

Immortal love, for ever full 109

PROPER 6 - B

I am a new creation 105
Love divine, all loves excelling 143
My Jesus, my Saviour 153
The Church's one foundation 212

PROPER 7 - B

Be still, my soul 33
Eternal Father, strong to save 65
Give thanks with
    a grateful heart 80
I cannot tell 106
Lead us, heavenly Father,
    lead us 131

PROPER 8 - B

Abba, Father, let me be 1
Love divine, all loves excelling 143
New every morning is the love 156

PROPER 9 - B

Give thanks with a
    grateful heart 80
Glorious things of thee
    are spoken 81
Lord of all hopefulness 140
O God, our help in ages past 168
Thy hand, O God, has guided 231

PROPER 10 - B

Fill your hearts with joy
    and gladness 73
King of glory, King of peace 129
Make way, make way 148
We love the place, O God 240

PROPER 11 - B

All for Jesus! 8
Bread of heaven,
    on thee we feed 39
Christ is made the
    sure foundation 44
Christ is our cornerstone 45
Faithful Shepherd, feed me 66
Father, hear the prayer we offer 67
In heavenly love abiding 111
The King of love my shepherd is 217
The Lord's my shepherd 218

PROPER 12 - B

All my hope on God is founded 13
Bread of heaven, on thee we feed 39
Eternal Father, strong to save 65
Just as I am, without one plea 128

PROPER 13 - B

Alleluia, sing to Jesus 7
Bread of heaven, on thee we feed 39
Glorious things of
    thee are spoken 81
Guide me,
    O thou great Redeemer 90
My God, and is
    thy table spread 151
The Church's one foundation 212
Thy hand, O God, has guided 231

PROPER 14 - B

Bread of heaven, on thee we feed 39
Come on and celebrate 54
Oft in danger, oft in woe 166
Through all the changing
    scenes of life 229

PROPER 15 - B

Awake, my soul,
    and with the sun 30
Bread of heaven, on thee we feed 39
My God, and is thy table spread 151

PROPER 16 - B

Alleluia, alleluia,
    give thanks to the risen Lord 5
Be thou my vision 35
Soldiers of Christ, arise 201
There is a Redeemer 220
Through all the changing
    scenes of life 229

PROPER 17 - B

All my hope on God is founded 13
Be still my soul 33
Fight the good fight 72
Great is thy faithfulness 89
Hail to the Lord's anointed 92
O strength and stay 182

PROPER 18 - B

All things bright and beautiful 16

Come, ye faithful,
    raise the anthem 57

PROPER 19 - B

All heaven declares 11
All things bright and beautiful 16
As the deer pants for the water 25

PROPER 20 - B

From heaven you came 78
Teach me, my God and King 209

PROPER 21 - B

As the deer pants for the water 25
O God, our help in ages past 168

PROPER 22 - B

All hail the power of Jesus' name 10
Be still, for the presence
    of the Lord 32
Be thou my guardian
    and my guide 34
Jesus shall reign
    where'er the sun 125
Meekness and majesty 149
O Lord, my God 172
We love the place, O God 240

PROPER 23 - B

Blessed assurance, Jesus is mine 37
How sweet the name of
    Jesus sounds 104
O God, our help in ages past 168

PROPER 24 - B

Bread of heaven, on thee we feed 39
Eternal Father, strong to save 65
From heaven you came 78
Jesus is Lord! 123
Meekness and majesty 149
What a friend we have in Jesus 243

PROPER 25 - B

And now, O Father,
    mindful of the love 21
Once, only once,
    and once for all 176
Through all the changing
    scenes of life 229

Or: BIBLE SUNDAY - B

As the deer pants for the water 25
Put thou thy trust in God 192

DEDICATION FESTIVAL - B

Blessed assurance, Jesus is mine 37
Christ is made the
    sure foundation 44
Christ is our cornerstone 45
Light's abode, celestial Salem 135
Loving Shepherd of thy sheep 145
Nearer, my God, to thee 155

ALL SAINTS' DAY - B

Be still, my soul 33
Hills of the north, rejoice 98
Light's abode, celestial Salem 135
Oft in danger, oft in woe 166

The Church's one foundation 212
Thy kingdom come, O God 232
Ye choirs of new Jerusalem 249

**FOURTH SUNDAY
BEFORE ADVENT - B**

Alleluia, sing to Jesus 7

**THIRD SUNDAY BEFORE
ADVENT - B**

Dear Lord and Father
  of mankind 61
Jesus calls us: o'er the tumult 121

**SECOND SUNDAY
BEFORE ADVENT - B**

Be thou my vision 35
Jerusalem the golden 117

CHRIST THE KING - B

Angel voices ever singing 24
Come, let us join our
  cheerful songs 53
Come, ye faithful,
  raise the anthem 57
Crown him with many crowns 60
God is love, his the care 83
Immortal, invisible 109
Lo, he comes with clouds
  descending 136
O worship the King 184

YEAR C

ADVENT

FIRST SUNDAY OF ADVENT - C

Hark! a herald voice is calling 94
Jesu, lover of my soul 118
Ye servants of the Lord 252

**SECOND SUNDAY
OF ADVENT - C**

Christ, whose glory fills the skies 48

**FOURTH SUNDAY
OF ADVENT - C**

Tell out, my soul 210
The angel Gabriel from
  heaven came 211

CHRISTMAS

CHRISTMAS EVE - See YEAR A

**CHRISTMAS DAY - See YEAR A
FIRST SUNDAY
OF CHRISTMAS - C**

Angel voices ever singing 24
Bind us together, Lord 36
Come down, O Love divine 51
O praise ye the Lord 180
Praise, my soul,
  the King of heaven 188
Praise the Lord,
  ye heavens adore him 189
Ye holy angels bright 250

**SECOND SUNDAY
OF CHRISTMAS - See YEAR A**

EPIPHANY

THE EPIPHANY - See YEAR A

THE BAPTISM OF CHRIST - C

Do not be afraid 64

**SECOND SUNDAY
OF EPIPHANY - C**

Father of heaven,
  whose love profound 69
Immortal, invisible 109
Jesu, lover of my soul 118
Jesus is Lord! 123
Lord Jesus Christ 138

**THIRD SUNDAY
OF EPIPHANY - C**

All heaven declares 11
As the deer pants for the water 25
Bind us together, Lord 36
God's Spirit is in my heart 86
Hail to the Lord's anointed 92
Make way, make way 148
O for a thousand tongues
  to sing 164

**FOURTH SUNDAY
OF EPIPHANY - C**

Come, thou long-expected Jesus 56
Glorious things of thee
  are spoken 81
O God, our help in ages past 168
Thy hand, O God, has guided 231

**THE PRESENTATION OF
CHRIST IN THE TEMPLE -
See YEAR A**

ORDINARY TIME

PROPER 1 - C

A new commandment 22
Bright the vision that delighted 42
Dear Lord and Father
  of mankind 61
Immortal, invisible 109
I, the Lord of sea and sky 114
Lord, the light of your love 141

PROPER 2 - C

Blessed assurance, Jesus is mine 37
Make way, make way 148

PROPER 3 - C

Praise to the Holiest 190

**SECOND SUNDAY
BEFORE LENT - C**

Be still, my soul 33
Breathe on me, Breath of God 40
Eternal Father, strong to save 65
I cannot tell 106
O Breath of Life 159

**SUNDAY NEXT
BEFORE LENT - C**

Be still, for the presence
  of the Lord 32

Christ whose glory
  fills the skies 48
Lord, the light of your love 141

LENT

ASH WEDNESDAY - See YEAR A

FIRST SUNDAY OF LENT - C

All my hope on God
  is founded 13
Forty days and forty nights 77
Lead us, heavenly Father,
  lead us 131

SECOND SUNDAY OF LENT - C

Put thou thy trust in God 192
To be in your presence 233

THIRD SUNDAY OF LENT - C

Put thou thy trust in God 192
Rock of ages 196

FOURTH SUNDAY OF LENT - C

I am a new creation 105
Love divine, all loves excelling 143
The Church's one foundation 212

**Or: MOTHERING SUNDAY -
See YEAR A**

FIFTH SUNDAY OF LENT - C

And now, O Father,
  mindful of the love 21
Fight the good fight 72

PALM SUNDAY - C

Liturgy of the Palms

All glory, laud and honour 9
Christ is made the
  sure foundation 44
I will enter his gates 116
Ride on, ride on in majesty 195

Liturgy of the Passion

All ye who seek a comfort sure 17
And can it be 19
At the name of Jesus 29
Christ triumphant,
  ever reigning 47
From heaven you came 78
Meekness and majesty 149
My song is love unknown 154
O sacred head sore wounded 181
Praise to the Holiest 190
To the name of our salvation 236

**MONDAY OF HOLY WEEK -
See YEAR A**

**TUESDAY OF HOLY WEEK -
See YEAR A**

**WEDNESDAY OF HOLY WEEK -
See YEAR A**

**MAUNDY THURSDAY -
See YEAR A**

GOOD FRIDAY - See YEAR A

**EASTER EVE - See YEAR A
Services other than the Easter Vigil**

EASTER VIGIL - See YEAR A

EASTER DAY - C

Alleluia, alleluia, hearts to
  heaven and voices raise 6
Christ is made the
  sure foundation 44
I will enter his gates 116
Love's redeeming work is done 144
On this day, the first of days 179
Thine be the glory 223
This is the day 225

**SECOND SUNDAY
OF EASTER - C**

At the lamb's high feast we sing 28
Christ is made the
  sure foundation 44
Come, ye faithful, raise the strain 58
Crown him with many crowns 60
I will enter his gates 116
My God I love thee, not because 152
O praise ye the Lord 180
Praise to the Lord,
  the Almighty 191
Saviour, again to thy
  dear name we raise 197
Thine be the glory 223
This is the day 225

**THIRD SUNDAY
OF EASTER - C**

All heaven declares 11
Angel voices ever singing 24
Come, let us join our
  cheerful songs 53
Come, ye faithful,
  raise the anthem 57
Glorious things of thee
  are spoken 81
I cannot tell 106
Majesty, worship his majesty 146
Praise to the Lord, the Almighty 191
We have a gospel to proclaim 239
Ye servants of God 251

**FOURTH SUNDAY
OF EASTER - C**

All heaven declares 11
As we are gathered 26
At the Lamb's high feast we sing 28
Blessed assurance, Jesus is mine 37
Faithful Shepherd, feed me 66
Father, hear the prayer we offer 67
In heavenly love abiding 111
Jerusalem the golden 117
The King of love my shepherd is 217
The Lord's my shepherd 218
Ye servants of God 251

FIFTH SUNDAY OF EASTER - C

A new commandment 22
Angel voices, ever singing 24
Be still, my soul 33
Hills of the north, rejoice 98
Oft in danger, oft in woe 166
O praise ye the Lord 180
Peace, perfect peace, is the gift 186
Praise, my soul,
  the King of heaven 188

Praise the Lord,
   ye heavens adore him 189
The Church's one foundation 212
Thy kingdom come, O God 232
Ye choirs of new Jerusalem 249
Ye holy angels bright 250

SIXTH SUNDAY OF EASTER - C

Breathe on me, Breath of God 40
City of God, how broad and far 49
Come, thou Holy Spirit, come 55
Crown him with many crowns 60
God of mercy, God of grace 85
Guide me, O thou
   great Redeemer 90
Saviour, again to thy dear
   name we raise 197
Thou, whose almighty word 228

ASCENSION DAY - See YEAR A

**SEVENTH SUNDAY
OF EASTER - C**

As we are gathered 26
Christ, whose glory fills the skies 48
I, the Lord of sea and sky 114
Love divine, all loves excelling 143
Put thou thy trust in God 192
Rejoice, the Lord is King 194

PENTECOST (Whit Sunday) - C

Abba, Father, let me be 1
Angel voices, ever singing 24
Breathe on me, Breath of God 40
Come down, O Love divine 51
Come, Holy Ghost,
   our souls inspire 52
Come, thou Holy Spirit, come 55
Lord, the light of your love 141
O Breath of Life 159
Saviour, again to thy dear
   name we raise 197

ORDINARY TIME

TRINITY SUNDAY - C

Be thou my guardian
   and my guide 34
I am a new creation 105

Jesus shall reign
   where'er the sun 125
O Lord, my God 172

PROPER 4 - C

Father of heaven,
   whose love profound 69
We have a gospel to proclaim 239

PROPER 5 - C

Come, ye faithful,
   raise the anthem 57
Father of heaven,
   whose love profound 69

PROPER 6 - C

Alleluia, alleluia,
   give thanks to the risen Lord 5
Come on and celebrate 54
I danced in the morning 107
Lord, for the years 137

PROPER 7 - C

All my hope on God is founded 13
As the deer pants for the water 25
Jesu, lover of my soul 118

PROPER 8 - C

Be thou my vision 35
Dear Lord and Father
   of mankind 61
Jerusalem the golden 117
Thou didst leave they throne 227

PROPER 9 - C

Lord, for the years 137
When I survey the
   wondrous cross 246

PROPER 10 - C

Jesu, lover of my soul 118
Meekness and majesty 149
When I needed a neighbour 245

PROPER 11 - C

At the name of Jesus 29

PROPER 12 - C

Bread of heaven, on thee we feed 39
Fill your hearts with joy
   and gladness 73
Make me a channel
   of your peace 147
Thy kingdom come, O God 232
We love the place, O God 240

PROPER 14 - C

O God, our help in ages past 168
Ye servants of the Lord 252

PROPER 16 - C

For all the saints 75
Praise, my soul,
   the King of heaven 188

PROPER 17 - C

All my hope on God is founded 13
For the beauty of the earth 76

PROPER 19 - C

Amazing grace 18
Immortal, invisible 109
Meekness and majesty 149
The King of love
   my shepherd is 217

PROPER 20 - C

Stand up, stand up for Jesus 205

PROPER 21 - C

All my hope on God is founded 13
Come, ye faithful
   raise the anthem 57
Fight the good fight 72
Jesu, lover of my soul 118

PROPER 22 - C

We have a gospel to proclaim 239

PROPER 23 - C

All my hope on God is founded 13
Lord of all hopefulness 140

PROPER 24 - C

All my hope on God is founded 13
Lord, thy word abideth 142

PROPER 25 - C

Alleluia, alleluia,
   give thanks to the risen Lord 5
Come, ye faithful,
   raise the anthem 57
Fight the good fight 72
Soldiers of Christ, arise 201

Or: BIBLE SUNDAY - C

God's Spirit is in my heart 86
Hail to the Lord's anointed 92
Make way, make way 148
O for a thousand
   tongues to sing 164

DEDICATION FESTIVAL - C

Angel voices, ever singing 24

ALL SAINTS' DAY - C

Come, ye faithful,
   raise the anthem 57
Make way, make way 148

**FOURTH SUNDAY
BEFORE ADVENT - C**

At the name of Jesus 29
The Spirit lives to set us free 221

**SECOND SUNDAY
BEFORE ADVENT - C**

Christ, whose glory fills the skies 48

CHRIST THE KING - C

All ye who seek a comfort sure 17
At the name of Jesus 29
Glorious things of thee
   are spoken 81
Immortal love, for ever full 110
Meekness and majesty 149
My Jesus, my Saviour 153
O God, our help in ages past 168

Index of First Lines

This index gives the first line of each hymn.
If a hymn is known also by a title (e.g. Jerusalem)
this is given as well, but indented and in italics.

A

Abba, Father, let me be   1
Abide with me   2
A great and mighty wonder   3
All creatures of our God and King   4
Alleluia, alleluia, give thanks to the risen Lord   5
Alleluia, alleluia, hearts to heaven
    and voices raise   6
Alleluia, sing to Jesus   7
All for Jesus!   8
All glory, laud and honour   9
All hail the power of Jesus' name   10
All heaven declares   11
All I once held dear   12
All my hope on God is founded   13
All over the world   14
All people that on earth do dwell   15
All things bright and beautiful   16
All you who seek a comfort sure   17
Amazing grace   18
And can it be   19
And did those feet in ancient time   20
And now, O Father, mindful of the love   21
A new commandment   22
Angels from the realms of glory   23
Angel-voices ever singing   24
As the deer pants for the water   25
As we are gathered   26
As with gladness men of old   27
At the Lamb's high feast we sing   28
At the name of Jesus   29
Awake, my soul, and with the sun   30
Away in a manger   31

B

Be still, for the presence of the Lord   32
Be still, my soul   33
Be thou my guardian and my guide   34
Be thou my vision   35
Bind us together, Lord   36
Blessed assurance   37
Blest are the pure in heart   38
Bread of heaven, on thee we feed   39
Breathe on me, Breath of God   40
Brightest and best   41
Bright the vision that delighted   42

C

Christians, awake!   43
Christ is made the sure foundation   44
Christ is our cornerstone   45
Christ the Lord is risen again   46
Christ triumphant   47
Christ, whose glory fills the skies   48
City of God, how broad and far   49
Colours of day   50
Come down, O Love divine   51
Come, Holy Ghost, our souls inspire   52
Come, let us join our cheerful songs   53
Come on and celebrate   54
Come, thou Holy Spirit, come   55
Come, thou long-expected Jesus   56
Come, ye faithful, raise the anthem   57
Come, ye faithful, raise the strain   58
Come, ye thankful people, come   59
Crown him with many crowns   60

D

Dear Lord and Father of mankind   61
Ding dong, merrily on high!   62
Disposer supreme   63
Do not be afraid   64

E

Eternal Father, strong to save   65

F

Faithful Shepherd, feed me   66
Father, hear the prayer we offer   67
Father, I place into your hands   68
Father of heaven, whose love profound   69
Father, we adore you   70
Father, we love you   71
Fight the good fight   72
Fill your hearts with joy and gladness   73
Firmly I believe and truly   74
For all the saints   75
For the beauty of the earth   76
Forty days and forty nights   77
From heaven you came   78

G

Give me joy in my heart   79
Give thanks with a grateful heart   80
Glorify your name   71
Glorious things of thee are spoken   81
God be in my head   82
God is love: his the care   83
God moves in a mysterious way   84
God of mercy, God of grace   85
God's Spirit is in my heart   86
Go forth and tell   87
Good King Wenceslas   88
Go, tell everyone   86
Great is thy faithfulness   89
Guide me, O thou great Redeemer   90

H

Hail the day that sees him rise   91
Hail to the Lord's anointed   92
Hallelujah, my Father   93
Hark! a herald voice is calling   94
Hark, the glad sound!   95
Hark, the herald-angels sing   96
He has made me glad   116
Here I am, Lord   114
He who would valiant be   97
Hills of the north, rejoice   98
Holy, holy, holy! Lord God almighty   99
Hosanna, hosanna   100
How deep the Father's love for us   101
How firm a foundation   102
How great thou art   172
How lovely on the mountains   103
How sweet the name of Jesus sounds   104

I

I am a new creation   105
I cannot tell   106
I danced in the morning   107
I heard the voice of Jesus say   108
Immortal, invisible, God only wise   109
Immortal love, for ever full   110
In heavenly love abiding   111
In the bleak mid-winter   112
It came upon the midnight clear   113
I, the Lord of sea and sky   114

It is a thing most wonderful   115
I will enter his gates   116

J

Jerusalem   20
Jerusalem the golden   117
Jesu, lover of my soul   118
Jesus calls us: o'er the tumult   119
Jesus Christ   120
Jesus Christ is risen today   121
Jesus, good above all other   122
Jesus is Lord! Creation's voice proclaims it   123
Jesus lives! thy terrors now   124
Jesus shall reign   125
Jesu, the very thought of thee   126
Jubilate, everybody   127
Just as I am, without one plea   128

K

King of glory, King of peace   129
Knowing you   12

L

Lead, kindly light   130
Lead us, heavenly Father, lead us   131
Let all the world in every corner sing   132
Let us, with a gladsome mind   133
Lift high the Cross   134
Light's abode, celestial Salem   135
Light up the fire   50
Living Lord   138
Lo, he comes with clouds descending   136
Lord, for the years   137
Lord Jesus Christ   138
Lord Jesus, think on me   139
Lord of all hopefulness   140
Lord of the dance   107
Lord, the light of your love   141
Lord, thy word abideth   142
Love divine, all loves excelling   143
Love's redeeming work is done   144
Loving Shepherd of thy sheep   145

M

Majesty, worship his majesty   146
Make me a channel of your peace   147
Make way, make way   148
Meekness and majesty   149
Morning has broken   150
My desire   233
My God, and is thy table spread   151
My God, I love thee   152
My Jesus, my Saviour   153
My song is love unknown   154

N

Nearer, my God, to thee   155
New every morning is the love   156
Now thank we all our God   157
Now the green blade riseth   158

O

O Breath of Life   159
O come, all ye faithful   160
O come, O come, Emmanuel   161
O dearest Lord, thy sacred head   162
O for a closer walk with God   163
O for a thousand tongues to sing   164
Of the Father's love begotten   165
Oft in danger, oft in woe   166
O God beyond all praising   167

O God, our help in ages past 168
O happy band of pilgrims 169
O Jesus, I have promised 170
O little town of Bethlehem 171
O Lord, my God 172
O Love that wilt not let me go 173
On a hill far away 174
Once in royal David's city 175
Once, only once, and once for all 176
On Christmas night all Christians sing 177
Once again 120
One more step along the world I go 178
On this day, the first of days 179
O praise ye the Lord! 180
O sacred head sore wounded 181
O strength and stay 182
O thou who camest from above 183
Our God reigns 103
O worship the King 184
O worship the Lord in the beauty of holiness 185

P

Peace, perfect peace, is the gift 186
Praise him 187
Praise, my soul, the King of heaven 188
Praise the Lord, ye heavens, adore him 189
Praise to the Holiest 190
Praise to the Lord, the Almighty 191
Put thou thy trust in God 192

R

Rejoice, O land, in God thy might 193
Rejoice, the Lord is King 194
Ride on, ride on in majesty 195
Rock of ages 196

S

Saviour, again to thy dear name we raise 197
See, amid the winter's snow 198
See him lying on a bed of straw 199
Shine, Jesus, shine 141
Shout to the Lord 153
Silent night 200
Sing hosanna 79
Soldiers of Christ, arise 201
Songs of thankfulness and praise 202
Spirit of the living God 203
Stand up and bless the Lord 204
Stand up, stand up for Jesus 205
Such love 206
Sun of my soul, thou Saviour dear 207

T

Take up thy cross, the Saviour said 208
Teach me, my God and King 209
Tell out, my soul 210
The angel Gabriel from heaven came 211
The Church's one foundation 212
The day of resurrection 213
The day thou gavest, Lord, is ended 214
The first Nowell 215
The head that once was crowned with thorns 216
The King of love my shepherd is 217
The Lord's my shepherd 218
The old rugged cross 174
There is a green hill far away 219
There is a Redeemer 220
The Servant King 78
The Spirit lives to set us free 221
The strife is o'er, the battle done 222
The trees of the field 253
Thine be the glory 223

Thine for ever! God of love 224
This is the day 225
This is your God 149
This joyful Eastertide 226
Thou didst leave thy throne 227
Thou, whose almighty word 228
Through all the changing scenes of life 229
Through the night of doubt and sorrow 230
Thy hand, O God, has guided 231
Thy kingdom come, O God 232
To be in your presence 233
To God be the glory! 234
To thee, O Lord, our hearts we raise 235
To the name of our salvation 236

U

Unto us a boy is born 237

W

Walk in the light 221
We are marching 238
We have a gospel to proclaim 239
We love the place, O God 240
We plough the fields and scatter 241
We three kings of Orient are 242
What a friend we have in Jesus 243
When all thy mercies, O my God 244
When I needed a neighbour 245
When I survey the wondrous cross 246
While shepherds watched 247
Will your anchor hold 248

Y

Ye choirs of new Jerusalem 249
Ye holy angels bright 250
Ye servants of God 251
Ye servants of the Lord 252
You shall go out with joy 253